Thanks to everyone who made *Spirituality for Badasses Book 1* a best-selling, award-winning underground hit! I suggest reading *it* first before diving into *The Workbook*. Buy it, share it and shout about it using the web sites below. Thanks!

- J. Stewart

Search "Spirituality for Badasses":
Audible
Amazon-US, Amazon-CA, Amazon-UK
Kobo, Barnes & Noble, Powell's, Books-a-Million

Share it:
Facebook–	Spirituality for BA
YouTube–	Spirituality for Badasses
Instagram–	JStewartDixon
Twitter–	JStewartDixon
Pinterest–	Spirituality for Badasses

Read & Engage   **Listen**

THIS BOOK INCLUDES AUDIO LESSONS

Use them. They'll change your life.

Spirituality for Badasses The Workbook is enhanced by audio file lessons. Use them! You'll get *good* results if you engage with the reading material, but you'll get *life-changing* results if you also engage with the audio file lessons. When you see the symbol below, that's your cue to stop reading and start listening. (You also have the option to upgrade to video.)

EMAIL ACCOUNT REQUIRED FOR ACCESS TO AUDIO FILES

In order to access the audio files safely, easily, and on any device, you'll need to create a simple free account with email and password. Go to the back of this book (page 281) where you'll find instructions on how to do this.

Review, Share & Shout !

Make the world a more spiritual badass place: After reading, please leave a review with your thoughts, opinions and stars. Just search *Amazon* for **Spirituality for Badasses The Workbook** and spread the love baby. Thanks and enjoy the ride !

SFB FAN & READER REVIEWS

It isn't often that one book can make me smile, bring me to tears and make me think… thank you & congrats! **–Henri**

Love me some Lenny!!! Great book!!! Great ride!!! ♥ **– Ric**

I'm very skeptical of FACEBOOK ADS, I'm glad I took a leap and ordered this!! Got my copy a couple months ago... I've read it twice!! HIGHLY RECOMMENDED!!**–Chris**

Is there a book 2? Because I must have it! ♥ **–Heather**

Bought it through audible and I love it **–Gabriela**

Loved it. Now I want to go to that retreat! **–Melody**

I just read it in 2 days. Looking forward to #2 **–Amy**

I just started reading this book and so far it's amazing!! **–Deaneen**

Great listen on audible. Lenny is my new best friend. Can't wait for more. **–Graham**

Just received my book from Amazon, read the first few pages and am hooked! Can't wait for the weekend so I can binge read the whole thing! **–Megan**

It's an amazing adventure. **–Tanya**

Good book and I love the audible version **–Madara**

It's awesome 👣 🐾 –**Linda**

This is such a fantastic book. I really enjoyed reading it. –**Nancy**

Great read. Not too many books that I plan to read a second time but this is definitely one of them. –**Jay**

Incredible book! As a true badass I learned a lot and it has really come in handy the last few days. Going to recommend it to my veteran group. I can't wait to hear more about the lizard 🦎 –**Francis**

Listened to this book on audible. AWESOME listen!!!! –**Roxane**

This book spoke to my core. So much so, I sent one to my brother. 💜 –**Jackie**

I'm currently reading this on Amazon kindle but I will defiantly be purchasing paperback!!! It's amazing –**Andrea**

I am reading this currently. I really enjoy the way that it is written! And it's funny! I recommend! –**Tonya**

I love this book!! I'm currently reading it and it's awesome!! –**Lauren**

This is so worth listening to absolutely great narrative and funny –**Chris**

Wouldn't Preparation H be more effective? –**Moses**

Half way through and feeling enlightened. An excellent read –**Angelo**

This book is amazing! On my second time through it!–**Valerie**

I just got this and not too far into it ..but so far, I absolutely love this book! 💜 –**Rebecca**

Just finished the book. There is now so much to ponder. Gratitude! –**Leigh**

Absolutely love this book X –**Helen**

SFB PROFESSIONAL REVIEWS

"*Spirituality for Badasses* should be part of any self-help, spirituality, or mindfulness collection. It goes where no other books in these genres dare travel, doing so ... in a way no other book matches."

–Midwest Book Review

"Dixon has much to offer, repackaging mysticism, intentionality, and self-care into something proudly lowbrow and accessible. ... A jokey yet earnest and useful guide to enlightenment for badass readers."

– Kirkus Reviews

"(Dixon) has clearly done his spiritual homework and he succeeds at distilling the effective and life-changing ingredients of contemplation and initiation. His relationship to his student/reader is like a shaman drill sergeant cajoling and nudging and ultimately getting his team over the hurdle."

–Pacific Book Review

"It's this shedding of typical, formalist intonations and the possession of a good sense of fun that makes *Spirituality for Badasses*, along with J. Stewart Dixon, entertaining – but never at the expense of holistically sharing material. That's to be commended."

–The Magic Pen

DISCLAIMER

The written contents of this book and the audio files that accompany it are for informational and educational purposes only and are not a substitute for professional medical advice, treatment or therapy. Consult a medical professional or healthcare provider if you are in need of medical advice, diagnoses, or treatment. PIE Publishing, Awakening Resources, LLC and J. Stewart Dixon are not liable for risks or issues associated with using or acting upon the information in this book.

SPIRITUALITY
for
Badasses
The WorkBook

HOW TO FIND INNER PEACE & HAPPINESS
WITHOUT LOSING YOUR COOL

The
WORKBOOK

J. Stewart Dixon

PhE
publishing

THE WORKBOOK 1ST EDITION

ISBN Ebook: 978-0-9858579-4-3

ISBN Paperback: 978-0-9858579-2-9

Any references to historical events, real people, or real places are used fictitiously. Names, characters, and places are products of the author's imagination.

Cover design by J. Stewart Dixon & Darren Wheeling
www.blackegg.com

Edited by Mary Lib Morgan
www.perfectlypenned4you.com

PIE Publishing
Charlottesville, VA
www.spiritualityforbadasses.com

Contents

PART 1: *Attention Lessons*

1. Why Are You Here?   19
How to fess up
2. The Sobering Truth– AUDIO Only   39
How to sit down, shut-up and get your Zen on.
3. Motivation & Lying   41
How to find motivation and how to stop lying
4. The Denial of Death   49
How to overcome denial
5. Ooh Shiny Pretty Objects!!   57
How to overcome constant distraction
6. The Night Sky– AUDIO Only   61
How to ask & answer the BIG questions
7. Your Emotional Brain   63
How to be emotionally intelligent
8. Your Thoughts Aren't Original   71
How to separate yourself from your thoughts
9. Body Attention & AUDIO   79
How to relax your flawed body
    Write Me a Letter   84

PART 2: *Awareness Lessons*

10. Evolutionary Refresher Course   89
How to be more aware and evolve the lack
11. Evolution's Invitation & AUDIO   95
How to be aware of your invitation
12. Candles & Broomsticks & AUDIO   101
How to be aware while seeing & smelling
13. Oranges & Batwings & AUDIO   105
How to be aware while touching & tasting
14. Sonic Booms & Tibetan Bells & AUDIO   111
How to be aware while hearing & listening
15. Moving & Break Dancing & AUDIO   115
How to be aware while moving your body
16. Pissed Off & Blissed Out & AUDIO   121
How to be aware during all emotions
17. Think on These Things & AUDIO   127
How to be divorce your thoughts
    Write Me a Letter   133

PART 3: Mindfulness Lessons

18. What is Mindfulness?   139
How to live a mindful life
19. General Body Scan & AUDIO   143
How to lie down and be mindful
20. Thought Body Scan & AUDIO   153
How to be mindful of thoughts
21. Emotion Body Scan & AUDIO   165
How to be mindful of emotions
22. Pain Body Scan & AUDIO   177
How to be mindful of pain
23. Mindful Smart Phone & AUDIO   189
How to butt-dial mindfully
24. Mindful Mouth & AUDIO   195
How to eat, drink and smoke mindfully
25. Mindful Activity & AUDIO   201
How to do every day shit mindfully
    Write Me a Letter   207

PART 4: Ego Lessons

26. Ego Sobering Truth & AUDIO   213
How to recognize the constant activity of ego
27. Freefall & AUDIO   221
How to let go of everything
28. Seeing External Ego & AUDIO   229
How to let go of external things
29. Seeing Internal Ego & AUDIO   239
How to let go of internal things
30. Tattoo Therapy & AUDIO   249
How to heal and love yourself
31. Riding Roller Coasters & AUDIO   261
How to meet deep fear
32. Mindful Tequila & AUDIO   275
How to drink tequila like a spiritual badass
    Write Me a Letter   279

Author   282
Fan Reviews & Sharing   283
References   284
Book 2 Sneak Preview   285

This is an exercise workbook.
WORK. Book.

Eyes on the road, please.

Keep driving friend.

Awesome. We're headed to the top of that mountain.

So, this is a workbook. *Work.* Book.

Work …

Yeah, I hate that word too, but it's a fact of life: No worky; no getty.

To get the spiritual badass goods, you gotta do the spiritual badass work. If *Spirituality for Badasses Book 1* was your first spiritual book (or among your first), let's be real: Reading it was like drinking a White Claw. Have you ever had a White Claw? Seems innocent enough at first. Goes down easily. Lots of sugar. Great taste. But—Oopsy-doop! Drink two or three cans of that 8% alcohol hard-ass seltzer and you're smackdown, wobbly-eyed, liver-punished, delivered, and drunk. In other words, *Spirituality for Badasses* can pack a mighty punch—sometimes.

Maybe it did?

Or, okay, maybe it didn't? Maybe you read it and were like… *Meh—nice story; funny, insightful, but it didn't really affect me much.*

Either way. All good. Still…

Here you are—reading the introduction to this workbook. You must be looking for something, right?

You wanna take this spiritual badass stuff to the next level? You wanna get down and dirty?! You wanna ride the *actual* Fury 325 roller coaster?! You want the actual *Spirituality for Badasses* experience, and you want it to improve your life?! Is this you? Cool. This workbook can *absolutely* help you.

The lessons in this workbook will teach you to:

- Pay attention to your life, emotions, thoughts & body.
- Become acutely, amazingly aware of awareness.
- Be more mindful, patient & resilient.
- Understand and rise above the limitations of ego and mind.

If you follow the lessons, do the exercises, and listen to the audio files (or watch the videos) you will experience more of these awesome things:

- Peace, happiness, confidence, meaning, clarity, resolve, freedom & joy.

Are you ready and willing!? If so, this Jeep goes *all the way* to the top of the spiritual badass mountain. Nope…we don't go *on the shiny outside*. We go through the dark, scary interior.

This ain't no White Claw.

This is 200-year-old Scotch Whiskey.

Welcome friend.

This workbook is easy. Trust me, you can't screw it up.

I've catered this workbook experience to your numerous selves, so it's easy to do and hard to screw up. *All of you* is invited here: Your lazy-ass-self, your normal-self, your badass-self, and your spiritual-badass-self.

In other words, there's some gold here for *all* your fractured, separate, depressed, hurting, wounded, normal, down-to-earth, amazing, awesome, intelligent, aware, and courageous parts.

This workbook is composed of a wide variety of things to do: read, check, highlight, write, journal, listen to audios, and should you desire – watch videos.

I'm not going to give you a long-winded explanation of exactly how this workbook will go. It ain't rocket science. Just follow along. The only requirement is that you read *Spirituality for Badasses Book 1* first. (Why in the world you'd be reading this workbook before having read *Spirituality for Badasses* is beyond me, but gawd bless your crazy little soul– please go read *Spirituality for Badasses* right now.)

Things to do & get for the best badass experience:

- Choose a device to listen to the audio files with.
- Get some bad-ass headphones.
- If you upgrade to video– Use an iPad, Kindle or tablet. (I think most phones are too small.)
- Keep a pen or pencil handy.

- If you aren't a prolific note taker or journal writer– there should be enough room in this workbook for you to jot some things down.
- If you *are* a prolific note taker– consider purchasing a separate blank notebook or journal.
- Purchase four envelopes and stamps.
- Find a quiet, comfy place to sit or lie down while listening to the guided exercises.

How to access the audio files:

To access the accompanying audio files that complement and complete this workbook, go to the back of this workbook (page 281) where you'll find a web address. Go to the web address, follow the instructions there and create an account. It's super simple. Then, while reading this workbook, whenever you see the symbol below go find the corresponding audio file on your account and listen.

Prefer VIDEO over audio?

That's cool. I got you covered. Go register for the free audio files. Once you get into the platform where the audio files are held, you'll have the option to upgrade to video. Super simple.

The Unchanged You:
A Mind-Blowing Insight

How do you get the audio files? To access the audio files that complement and complete this workbook, go to the back of this workbook (page 281) where you'll find a web address. Go to the web address, follow the instructions there and create an account. If you prefer video there's an option to upgrade.

Notes:

PART 1

Attention Lessons

LESSON 1
WHY ARE YOU HERE?

How to fess up

Why are you here? What do you *really* want? What motivated you to purchase this book? What's goin' on, man? Come on, be honest...

You'd think that most people, before they shelled out some bucks for a book, workbook, or online course called *Spirituality for Badasses,* would have already tackled—and answered—at least a few of these questions. Think again...

I've met countless people at meditation meetups, weekend mindfulness workshops, or yoga retreats who shelled out a lot more than the cost of a book, and had *zero* idea why they were there. In my non-humble badass opinion, this is sort of like showing up to the Super Bowl (in person, at the arena, after having paid thousands to get there) with no clue or concern for which teams are playing. I mean— why fucking bother, right?

Well, that ain't happening here. You're gonna pick a team. You're gonna root for the team, and you're gonna wave your flag, scream your lungs out, and stomp your feet to the blazing loud hard rock anthem of *We Will Rock You* before, during, and after every single play your team makes. You're gonna root for a team, alright. That team is YOU.

So, I'll ask you again. What's up? Why are you here?

Let's get to the bottom of this: Ahead of you is a long list of common reasons you *might* be here. Your first spiritual badass exercise is to read through the list and check the boxes of those which apply. Why do this? It's simple—you need to get to know your team. You need to place your attention exactly on...*why you are here.*

Why are you here? Exercise:

Time required: 10-15 Minutes

Preparation: Find a comfortable quiet space where you won't be disturbed. It's best to sit in a relaxed, comfortable position as you read and check off all the boxes that apply.

Task: Read through the list and check the boxes of the descriptions that apply.

Breathe: Begin by taking three deep breaths so that your answers come from *both* body and mind.

Depressed?

Major Depression or Major Depressive Disorder Major Depression or Major Depressive Disorder is generally diagnosed when five of the following symptoms occur for two weeks or longer: • Loss of interest or pleasure in most activities • Weight loss or gain • Sleep trouble • Physically or mentally restless, agitated, or sluggish • Tired & low energy • Feelings of guilt or worthlessness • Trouble concentrating • Suicidal thoughts	☐
Persistent Depressive Disorder Persistent Depressive Disorder is diagnosed when the following symptoms occur for two years or longer: • Appetite change – Not eating or overeating • Sleeping too much or too little • Lack of energy& general fatigue • Low self-esteem • Concentration problems	☐

• Hopelessness

Bipolar Disorder or Manic Depression
Bipolar Disorder is diagnosed when the symptoms of
Major Depression occur for two weeks or longer
accompanied by opposite *high or positive* mood swings:
• Loss of interest or pleasure in most activities
• Weight loss or gain
• Sleep trouble
• Physically or mentally restless, agitated, or sluggish
• Tired & low energy
• Feelings of guilt or worthlessness
• Trouble concentrating
• Suicidal thoughts
    VS.
• Elation
• High energy
• Manic enthusiasm
• Deluded optimism
• Up feelings & moods
• Delusions of grandeur
• Emotional highs
• Restless unbounded energy
• Unbridled and unbalanced energy

Seasonal Affective Disorder (SAD)
Seasonal Affective Disorder is diagnosed when the
symptoms of Major Depression occur for two weeks
or longer during the winter months.
• Loss of interest or pleasure in most activities
• Weight loss or gain
• Sleep trouble
• Physically or mentally restless, agitated, or sluggish
• Tired & low energy
• Feelings of guilt or worthlessness
• Trouble concentrating

Psychotic Depression
Psychotic comes from psychosis which is defined as
follows: *a serious mental illness marked by loss
of or greatly lessoned ability to test whether what one is
thinking and feeling about the real world is
really true.* Psychotic Depression is diagnosed when the
symptoms of Major Depression occur for two
weeks or longer accompanied by psychotic symptoms:
• Loss of interest or pleasure in most activities

21

- Weight loss or gain
- Sleep trouble
- Physically or mentally restless, agitated, or sluggish
- Tired & low energy
- Feelings of guilt or worthlessness
- Trouble concentrating
- Suicidal thoughts
  Accompanied by:
- Hallucinations
- Delusions
- Paranoia
- Fantasies
- Disturbing thoughts or voices
- Disturbance by illusions, dreams, or fleeting distractions

Post-Partum Depression
Post-Partum Depression is diagnosed when the symptoms of Major Depression occur for two weeks or longer after childbirth:
- Loss of interest or pleasure in most activities
- Weight loss or gain
- Sleep trouble
- Physically or mentally restless, agitated, or sluggish
- Tired & low energy
- Feelings of guilt or worthlessness
- Trouble concentrating
- Suicidal thoughts

Premenstrual Dysphoric Disorder
Premenstrual Dysphoric Disorder is diagnosed when the following symptoms occur prior to the onset of menstruation and usually resolve with its onset:
- Low level depression or mood
- Mood swings
- Irritability
- Anxiety
- Trouble concentrating
- Fatigue
- Appetite problems
- Sleep problems
- Overwhelm

Situational Depression
Situational Depression is diagnosed when the following symptoms occur alongside a particular life event:
- Feelings of hopelessness

- Sadness
- Frequent Crying
- Anxiety
- Worry
- Headaches
- Stomachaches
  Accompanied by:
- Death in the family
- Divorce
- Loss of job
- Developing a serious illness
- Being a victim of a crime
- Having an accident
- Retirement
- Giving birth
- Living through a natural disaster such as fire, flood, or hurricane

Atypical Depression

Atypical Depression is diagnosed when the following symptoms occur:
- Sleeping too much
- Increased appetite or weight gain
- Increased sensitivity to rejection or criticism
- Having a feeling of paralysis, being weighed down, or leaden

Existential Depression

Existential Depression is diagnosed by neither the medical nor psychiatric community. This is an alternative descriptor of numerous states used regularly by religious and/or spiritual communities: sin, separation, unhappiness, dark night of the soul, zen sickness, soul rot, *something is missing, life is not good enough*, and suffering.

What distinguishes existential depression from other types of depression is that the one burdened by it does not necessarily feel randomly or mysteriously victimized by it. There is a clear objective capacity to see the depression as a positive part of personal growth or evolution.

The symptoms of existential depression mirror many symptoms of the nine other types of depression and are as follows:
- Loss of interest or pleasure in most activities
- Weight loss or gain

- Sleep trouble
- Physically or mentally restless, agitated, or sluggish
- Tired & low energy
- Trouble concentrating
- Feelings of guilt or worthlessness
- Feeling incapable of love
- General unhappiness
- Despair
- Anxiety
- Anxiety attacks
- Deep fear
- Chills and horror
- Feelings of imminent death
- Feelings of paralysis, being weighed down, or leaden
- Feelings of hopelessness
- Sadness
- Frequent Crying
- Worry
- Headaches
- Stomachaches

ARE YOU HAVING DANGEROUS SYMPTOMS?

If you are experiencing major depression with suicidal thoughts, are severely bipolar, or are suffering from psychotic depression, you need to seek out nearby professional help from a doctor, counselor, or therapist. And while *Spirituality for Badasses* can be of great benefit to you, please do not rely on it alone to navigate through the complexities of your situation. I am not anti-western medicine. I am not anti-therapy. Nor am I a doctor. Major depression with suicidal thoughts, severe bipolar disorder, and psychotic depression all demand the greatest care, multiple points of view, and—most importantly— a real-world hand and heart to help you navigate through it. Be smart. Be wary. Be wise. Get help.

Plain Old Unhappy or Stressed?

Unhappy	☐
Anxious	☐
Stressed	☐
Sad	☐
Grieving	☐
Frustrated	☐
Angry	☐
Lost	☐
Confused	☐
Lonely	☐
Bored	☐
Unmotivated, listless, and dead inside	☐
Fuck everything and everyone	☐

Emotionally Wounded?

Wounded from childhood	☐
Abused during childhood	☐
Unloved during childhood	☐
Neglected during childhood	☐
Childhood related insecurities	☐
Trust issues	☐
Angry, mad, or pissed off at close family	☐
Neglected, abused, or wounded by school, church, organization or authority figures	☐
Wounded from relationship	☐
Wounded from marriage or divorce	☐
Wounded from childhood bullying	☐
Wounded from adulthood bullying	☐
Anger management issues	☐

Long Time Spiritual Seeker?

Done it all and no results ☐

Read a thousand books, and still nothing ☐

Been to a bunch of workshops with minimal gain ☐

A few breakthroughs, but nothing permanent ☐

Meditation, yoga, and reading just isn't enough ☐

Studied with quite a few teachers and still seeking ☐

Burned by long-time relationship with a teacher ☐

Lots of cool experiences, but no true satisfaction ☐

Still seeking after all these years (decades) ☐

Fed up with the whole spiritual, new-age three ring circus ☐

Love spirituality, but ready to let the whole damn thing go ☐

I want to know the truth about myself, and don't give a shit how I get there ☐

Spiritual Seeker?

Seeking a spiritual experience, epiphany, insight, or high ☐

Seeking life's meaning or more meaning ☐

Searching for my life's purpose ☐

Looking for deeper connection to life ☐

Seeking enlightenment ☐

Seeking nondual awakening ☐

Seeking proof of life after death ☐

Seeking loved ones who have died ☐

Have used marijuana, mushrooms, or psychedelics ☐

Student of mindfulness ☐

Student of yoga ☐

Student of meditation ☐

Student of shamanism ☐

Student of Buddhism or Zen ☐

New to Spirituality?

This (SFB) is my first spiritual book ☐

Simply curious ☐

Seeking proof that there's something to spirituality ☐

Skeptic at heart, but open to spirituality ☐

Read a handful of books and am intrigued ☐

Seeking my first spiritual experience or breakthrough ☐

Seeking to be a better, happier, more positive person ☐

Want to know if there is an afterlife ☐

Seeking better mental and physical health through spirituality ☐

Seeking to live more in the present moment ☐

Heard about mindfulness and was interested ☐

Spiritual tire-kicking with no agenda or goal ☐

Religious Spiritual Seeker?

Religion or church has failed me	☐
Still a church member, but looking beyond it	☐
Attended church long ago, quit, and have been looking for something else ever since	☐
Religion or church still great but seeking something more	☐
Want nothing to do with organized religion but am seeking something	☐
Religion or church not deep or experiential enough for me	☐
Seeking a closer relationship with God, Jesus, Buddha, Mohammed, etc.	☐
Want to know if there is an afterlife	☐
Want to know if there is any truth at all to religion	☐
Total atheist or nonbeliever and wound up here somehow	☐

Do you think I'll attain supreme enlightenment, meet Jesus, and save the world?

For a variety of reasons—*fuck* no. But I do think you can be *happier*, maybe even *a lot happier.* Allow me to let you in on a little secret about the previous exercise. (You did it right? Checked off the boxes that applied to you? No!? Come on man. Ya gotta do the work, or this is just jerk-off worthless. Now, go get a pencil and check off those little boxes. I'm watching. Do it now. Gooo get a pencil...)

Where were we? Oh, right—secret about the previous exercise: There are really just two things that human beings seek in life. We seek to avoid pain, and we seek to find pleasure. The check boxes in the previous exercise all fall into one of these two categories. As a matter of fact, I color-coded them. Look closely. Those in **bold print** are behaviors that are pain avoidant. Those in normal print are pleasure seeking.

I'm pointing this out to you because you need *both* for true spiritual progress to take place. In other words, if you're exclusively looking for golden spiritual cookies, rainbows, and puppy dogs...you're in trouble. This book probably isn't going to be of much use to you. You have to dig deep and find the *pain* which has brought you here: the pain you are seeking to avoid, get rid of, or transform.

Alternatively, if you're exclusively a cold bucket of suck and pain, and have zero hope for anything better, happier, lighter, or more at peace, then you're *also* in trouble. You have to believe that some sort of light exists at the end of the tunnel.

31

Again, I'm telling you all this because, for most spiritual seekers, it's better and wiser to have a balanced checklist of the reasons you are here. Look at your checklist. Is it balanced or imbalanced? If so, are you being honest? Do you need to dig deeper and find the pain? Or do you need to be shown a little light?

In my work, I've seen that most of us can *easily* find a bunch pain that we are seeking to avoid—if we are honest. We'll explore this pain in depth throughout this book. It's the *light* that's hard or tricky to find in the beginning. So, let's do something about that. Let's find your light. One easy way to do that is to point out your personal badass strengths. Super simple and effective. It's one of the main principles and handshakes of our adventure together, right? You're a badass. You know it. I know it. Well, okay—maybe you've forgotten it a little…so let your light shine down, baby…

Let your badass light shine down Exercise:

Time required: 5-10 Minutes

Preparation: Find a comfortable quiet space where you won't be disturbed. It's best to sit in a relaxed, comfortable position as you read, and check off the boxes that apply.

Task: Read through the list and check the boxes of those which apply.

Breathe: Begin by taking three deep breaths, so that your answers come from *both* body and mind.

I'm a BADASS because I'm:

- Accepting
- Adaptable
- Adventurous
- Agreeable
- Aware
- Artistic
- Balanced
- Beautiful
- Calm
- Caring
- Centered
- Charismatic
- Considerate
- Courageous
- Creative
- Curious
- Confident
- Dedicated
- Diligent
- Energetic
- Enthusiastic
- Fair-minded

Flexible ☐

Focused ☐

Friendly ☐

Fun ☐

Generous ☐

Honest ☐

Humble ☐

Humorous ☐

Imaginative ☐

Inquisitive ☐

Insightful ☐

Intuitive ☐

Kind ☐

Loving ☐

Open-minded ☐

Optimistic ☐

Passionate ☐

Patient ☐

Persistent ☐

Practical ☐

Proactive ☐

Rational ☐

Reasonable ☐

Reliable ☐

Responsible ☐

Self-confident ☐

Sociable ☐

Spiritual ☐

Spontaneous ☐

Sympathetic ☐

Strong ☐

Sporty ☐

Thoughtful ☐

Trustworthy ☐

Versatile ☐

Warmhearted ☐

Wise ☐

Witty ☐

Spiritual Badass Homework:

Grab a pen or pencil. Let's do some writing.

If you're a prolific note taker I suggest getting a blank notebook or journal at the grocery or supply store. Go buy one and keep it nearby. (Seriously—put it on your grocery list, and buy it next time you go out.) For most though, this paperback version should have enough space on the "Notes" pages for you to write on.

Okay– down to business: In your journal, write out (list them) all the reasons why you're here (your checked boxes). Also, write out a list of your personal badass strengths.

After each list, answer these questions:

- What pain do you wish to avoid, get rid of, or transform by becoming a spiritual badass?

- What is your most important personal strength, and how can it assist you in becoming a spiritual badass?

Why do this?

There's power in intention, clarity, and focus. Yep—by merely writing these things down you are empowering your efforts, clarifying your intentions, and making your goals real.

Well done, badass.

Well done.

Notes:

Notes:

LESSON 2
THE SOBERING TRUTH

How to sit down, shut up and get your ZEN on.

Lesson 2:
The Sobering Truth

Listen

How do you get the audio files? To access the audio files that complement and complete this workbook, go to the back of this workbook (page 281) where you'll find a web address. Go to the web address, follow the instructions there and create an account. If you prefer video there's an option to upgrade.

Notes:

LESSON 3
MOTIVATION & LYING

How to find motivation and how to stop lying

Before we get into all the beautiful little lies you tell, there's something else we have to do first. We have to address a conundrum. Most people who embark upon this grand spiritual badass journey run into it. It's this: How do you find the time, energy, or motivation to do all this when (because, let's be honest, your spiritual badass self ain't steering the ship yet) you have very little time, energy, or motivation? In other words, when you're stuck in quicksand, how do you get out of it?

I know this conundrum from my own personal experience. Depression was my quicksand. I found it really hard while depressed to find the motivation to *do something* that would get me *out* of my depression. So how did I do it? How did I get myself out of the quicksand conundrum? I'm going to answer this question with the exercise below. At multiple points during my spiritual badass journey, I used the techniques below to unstuck, unfuck, and unrut myself from the quicksand.

Finding Motivation Exercise:

Time required: 5-10 Minutes

Preparation: Find a comfortable quiet space where you won't be disturbed. It's best to sit in a relaxed, comfortable position as you read and check off the boxes that apply.

Task: Read through the list of motivational techniques, and check the boxes of those which most appeal to you. Try those first. Return here anytime to try new techniques.

Breathe: Begin by taking three deep breaths, so that your answers come from *both* body and mind.

Motivational Techniques:

Reward yourself
This is a classic, sure-fire motivational technique. After reading each chapter here and completing the exercises or watching the videos, choose from this list: Watch your favorite Netflix show; Go to Starbucks; Take a walk in nature; Take a hot shower; Give yourself something yummy, good, and relaxing as a reward.

Adopt a Daily Schedule
Every day at 4:20, instead of that glass of wine or other thing, read a chapter from this book and complete the exercises. Pick a time each day. Put it on your calendar. Stick to it.

Show respect and compassion for yourself
A big part of the spiritual badass process is having to take two steps backward in order to take one step forward. By simply knowing, allowing, and accepting that this stuff is tough, you'll go a long way toward making it easier. Don't beat yourself up. Be excellent to yourself.

Sign on the dotted line:
I _____ do hereby agree and declare to do whatever it takes to find, accept, love, and fist-bump my own internal, flawed, spiritual badass self.

Shout it from the rooftop
This is another classic, tried and true motivational technique: Make your self-improvement goal public. Tell a friend or family member about your spiritual badass goals and ambitions—and ask for their support. Very powerful.

Follow your hero
Take inspiration from others you know who have embarked upon or completed the spiritual badass journey. This can

be a friend, relative, author, teacher, therapist, coach, or spiritual counselor. Heroes get inspiration from other heroes.

Clarify and set a goal
Determine a very specific goal and reason for being here. Write it down and commit to it. Here are some examples: I want to be depression free. I want to be a happier person. I want to live more in the moment. I want more joy. I want less pain and conflict. I want to know my full spiritual badass self.

Keep a log or journal of your progress
Progress on your journey will *fuel more* progress. Noting and celebrating each step you take can be very powerful. So go get that journal I spoke of in the last chapter, and start making progress notes.

Have a daily intention
Ask yourself: Is today just going to meander and slip by like all the other days or are am I going to grab it by the horns and make it *my* day? Setting your intention early in the morning or the night before can help you take the daily steps necessary for finding your internal spiritual badass.

Take inspiration from your past self
You've seen and experienced difficulty before. And here you are now—free and clear of that particular difficulty. What did you do to resolve it then? Trust that the same resources are available to you now to resolve your current quicksand conundrums, difficulties, or issues. You did it before; you can do it again.

As noted in *Spirituality for Badasses Book 1*, this whole journey rests upon the foundation of attention. For most of us, attention is constantly being compromised by the lies we're telling ourselves and others. Let's fix this by placing our attention on these lies.

Attention on Lying Exercise:
Time required: 5-10 Minutes

Preparation: Find a comfortable quiet space where you won't be disturbed. It's best to sit in a relaxed, comfortable position as you read and check off the boxes that apply.

Task: Read through the list of lies below and check the boxes of the ones you tell the most.

Breathe: Begin by taking three deep breaths, so that your answers come from *both* body and mind.

Which external lies do you tell?

White Lies ☐
We use white lies with good intention and to avoid conflict: That dress looks beautiful on you, dear. Busy this weekend, sorry. I love that meatloaf dish your mom cooks. I'm okay working the weekend shift.

Ethical Lies ☐
We use ethical lies for the perceived greater good: There is no money in our vault, Mr. Bank Robber. I know karate and kung-fu; back off, Mr. Mugger. If I catch you littering here again, I'll have you fined a thousand dollars and imprisoned.

Cultural Social Lies ☐
We use cultural lies to please and appease others: Santa will deliver your toys tomorrow night, dear; he will come down the chimney. Sparky has gone to doggy heaven, dear. It's okay, Grandma is in a better place now.

Omission Lies ☐
We use omission lies when we want to hide something from someone: i.e., You go grocery shopping, but omit telling your spouse that you also bought a case of beer. You invite a close friend over for dinner, but omit telling her you invited three other close friends. At a job interview, you omit telling your potential employer that you were fired from your last job.

Bald-Faced Lies ☐
We use bald-faced lies to get attention: Three days ago, I hunted down and captured Bigfoot. I'm related to the president of the United States. I drive a Ferrari and won the Monaco Formula One race.

Fabricated Lies

We use fabricated lies for exaggeration purposes: I ran a fifty-mile marathon over the weekend. I won half a million dollars in the lottery yesterday. I make two million dollars a year with my side business. I have a genius level IQ.

Which internal lies do you tell?

Denial Lies

We use denial lies to falsely comfort and delude: I'm fine. Everything is okay. It will all be good soon. Everything is hunky-dory. Nothing wrong or bad here.

Fantasy Lies

We use fantasy lies to mislead ourselves, comfort ourselves, and refuse reality: If I stay positive, think positive, and act positive, everything will be positive.

Blame Lies

We use blame lies to avoid accountability, responsibility, and ownership: There's nothing I can do. It's not my fault. I'm not to blame. It's his (or her) fault.

Unworthiness Lies

We use unworthiness lies as a means of avoiding the challenges of true growth and transformation: I'm not good enough. I'm not worthy. I'm not capable. I'm not qualified. I'll never be good enough until I have or become this or that.

Martyr Lies

We use martyr lies to justify our isolation, loneliness and refusal to live, work, and play with others: If it weren't for me, nothing would get done. I'm the only one who can solve this. I'm a saint. I'm a martyr.

Misfit Lies

We use misfit lies to justify our isolation, loneliness, and refusal to live, work, and play with others: I don't fit in. I'm special. No one else has this problem. I'm all alone.

So, it goes without saying that if you lie to yourself about the quality and quantity of lies you tell others and yourself, you're...um ... doing yourself a disservice. But I feel *ya*—sometimes we just don't realize all the little lies we're spewing about. So do this:

Grab your journaling book. What's the one lie among all the checked lies on the list that you think you tell the most? Write down and describe the lie in your journal, and answer the following questions:

- Can I go a week without telling any more of these lies?

- What would the effect be if I stopped telling this lie?

Why do this?

The more you place your attention (reading, writing, check-box exercises, etc.) on your lying, the quicker the lies tend to dissipate and become unnecessary. Most lies are generated from fear. We falsely think *we have* to lie. On the contrary, it's *much* better to live openly and honestly. When we do this, a courageous and vast inner landscape of attention and awareness is revealed.

Notes:

Notes:

LESSON 4
THE DENIAL OF DEATH

How to overcome denial

Denial is an insidious thing, third in command below ignorance and fear. Denial is the uniquely human delusional capacity to selectively hide, cover up, or forget whatever true or false idea we see fit…in service of blind spots, ignorance, or fear. Today, ladies and gentlemen, the sky is purple; there will never be another cloudy day; disease no longer exists. Denial often serves our worst impulses: Denial of moral right and wrong served Adolf Hitler and his minions quite well.

Okay—I might be blowing denial way out of proportion here, but denial can certainly ruin your life: Got a strange feeling about that lump on your breast? Deny it and maybe it'll go away. Slightly concerned about your empty refrigerator and wallet? Deny both and maybe they'll magically fill up. Afraid to talk about death even though a loved one is clearly dying? Just don't talk about it and maybe it'll go away. Feeling depressed, unhappy, and joyless throughout most of your life? Deny that too—and maybe one day you'll wake up singing happy songs about bluebirds on your shoulders.

Let me be frank here: Denial will in no way serve your highest intentions or aspirations of knowing your inner spiritual badass. Denial has *got* to go. So, let's begin the process of weaning you off it. Time to place your *attention* on the things you deny.

Attention on Denial Exercise:

Time required: 10-15 Minutes

Preparation: Find a comfortable quiet space where you won't be disturbed. It's best to sit in a relaxed, comfortable position as you read and check off the boxes that apply.

Task: Read through the denial list below and check the boxes of the ones you experience most often.

Breathe: Begin by taking three deep breaths so that your answers come from *both* body and mind.

Circumstantial Denial

Loneliness
I'm not lonely. I'm fine being all by myself. I'm used to the isolation. I don't need anyone else. ☐

Loss
I'm okay with the loss of my parents. I'm fine that she left me. It's okay, I can find another job. I didn't need that big house anyway. ☐

Bad Relationship
Our relationship isn't bad; the counseling is working. Yes, we've split up a few times, but she's changed. ☐

Abuse
He can be angry sometimes, but he never hits me. She yells at the kids because she's tired from work. ☐

Dysfunction
We're doing okay even though Dad has been arrested several times now. I need to smoke pot to save my marriage. ☐

Addiction
I'll have one, maybe two drinks in the evening—that's it. I can quit anytime. Marijuana helps me stay focused and relaxed. ☐

Sickness ☐

I'll kick the cancer—I meditate every day. It's at most a
fracture, and I hate doctors. It's just a rash I'm not worried.

Health
I don't trust anything that quack prescribes. I looked it up
online, and I'll be fine. No, I don't need therapy—that's for
crazies and weaklings.

Opinions
What I think doesn't matter. My vote hardly counts. No one
is going to care about my asshole opinion. If I take a side
I'll cause conflict and be part of the problem.

Likes
Yes, I would prefer to live there, but can't afford it. What I
want or desire is not important. My husband won't like that
dish, so I never cook it.

Dislikes
I really can't stand that neighbor's dog, but will tolerate its
barking. I'm always so cold. Why won't she let me turn up
the heat? Every day we *have* to eat that kind of bread?!

Pleasures
I wish she would massage my shoulders at least
occasionally. It's been ages since I purchased new
furniture or took a vacation. I just want one small slice of
carrot cake.

Pain
Yes, it aches but I can take it. Right now, it's throbbing but I
refuse to take that medication. It's only been sore for a few
months now.

Cultural Denial

Race
I hate the fact that I'm from the middle east. If I talk street
and blend in, no one will notice that I'm Asian.

Skin Color
Just stay focused, no one will care that I am a black
American. I secretly hate my white freckled skin. I wish I
had more brown tone.

Body Form
If I were only thinner. If I weren't so tall and skinny. Why was I born with these hips and legs and this neck!?

Feminine Nature
Why even bother to dress up or comb my hair? I have lost touch with my own fierce feminine power. I used to be creative, caring, and giving.

Masculine Nature
No—don't, I'll just come off as an asshole. I can't express my true desire with her. I've lost touch with my drive, mission, and purpose.

Sexuality
There's no way I can admit that I'm attracted to her. I wish he would caress, hold, and kiss me the way he used to.

Status
Who gives a damn about where we live or if I have a career!? So what if my kids go to the poorest school in the city?

Class
I will not be like my neighbors. I'm not interested in fitting in or getting along. I refuse to be anything like them!

Education
Who cares if I graduate? What's in a degree anyway? So what if she's had training!? Who cares about college!?

Intelligence
So what if she's smarter than me? Smarty pants, fancy-word-using snob. I'm a quick learner, but that doesn't pay the bills.

Existential Denial

Fear
We run from that which we fear, both externally and internally.

Death
To deny death is to deny life.

52

Suffering
If I turn a blind eye to suffering, maybe it will go away.

Anxiety
It's just a small anxiety attack. Nothing to worry about.

Limitation
I will not admit any limitation, flaw, or wound.

Childhood Wounds
The past is the past. Why bother?

Body
I hate my body.

Emotion
I will be strong and stifle my emotions.

Thoughts
I am in control of my thoughts. I am in control …

Survival
I constantly pretend that I am doing more than surviving.

Struggle
I refuse to admit that life is filled with struggle and strife.

Insignificance
Looking into the infinite starry sky makes me aware of my insignificance.

Meaning
When I think about the meaning of my life, it depresses me…because I don't see it.

Depression
I am not depressed. No way. Not me.

During your spiritual badass adventure, you will inevitably do battle with denial. There's no getting around it. It's a natural and normal response to uncomfortable truths, both small and large.

In *Spirituality for Badasses Book 1* you, the reader, end up in a denial war which continues until the very end of the book. You push away and deny a large earthquake anxiety attack concerning your childhood past. You push and you push and you push until *finally* the trembling tidal wave of the earthquake breaks down your denial defenses and overtakes you. You succumb to it and are greatly relieved after it passes.

This is no metaphor. Denial is one of last great structural defenses of the ego as it fights tooth and nail to stay in control. And in case you hadn't realized it, *Spirituality for Badasses* is about removing ego from its controlling throne. Winter is coming...

Spiritual Badass Homework:

Journal: Write these questions out and fill in the blanks.

- I *frequently* deny_____.
- If I stop this denial, I just might_____.
- I *occasionally* deny_____.
- If I stop this denial, I just might_____.
- I *sometimes* deny_____.
- If I stop this denial, I just might_____.

Why do this?

If you can't see denial, you can't stop it. Placing your attention on denial through reading, writing, checking, and journaling allows you to recognize it when it shows up.

Notes:

Notes:

LESSON 5
OOH SHINY PRETTY OBJECTS!!

How to overcome constant distraction

Whenever I see someone texting or scrolling while driving, it makes my blood boil. I usually have to stop myself from rolling down my window and screaming out a stream of obscenities at the perp. *Why?* Because it's bad enough that they have zero capacity for distraction self-control, but in this instance their distraction is putting *my life and other lives* in danger. Cruising down the highway with your nose buried nonchalantly in a smartphone as you steer a two-ton rolling block of steel is just plain bad karma.

Here's a recap from *Spirituality for Badasses Book 1* about the two kinds of distraction we need to pay attention to:

"Hijacked distraction is where we should be paying attention to A, but then our attention is captured by B, and we veer off-course and pay attention to B instead. Our smartphones are a classic example of the B that hijacks our A.

Aimless distraction is classically what Buddhists call "monkey mind." This is where our attention should be on A, but instead it's unfocused and all over the place—on B, C, G, F, L, and Z."

If we don't put our constant capacity for distraction in check, there's no way we'll even *come close* to discovering our own unique spiritual badass. We won't have the time, energy, focus, or resolve. Distraction will get the better of us and destroy any spiritual badass aspirations we may have had. Yep, you're selling your soul for shiny pretty objects. It's that simple. Let's get your time and energy back by helping you to get a handle on distraction.

Attention on Distraction Exercise:

Time required: 5-10 Minutes

Preparation: Find a comfortable quiet space where you won't be disturbed. It's best to sit in a relaxed, comfortable position as you read and check off the boxes that apply.

Task: Read through the list of distractions below and check the boxes of the ones that most apply to you.

Breathe: Begin by taking three deep breaths so that your answers come from *both* body and mind.

Hijacked & Aimless Distraction

Smartphone Social Media
Obsessed with checking social media, posts, likes, responses, and interactions ☐

Smartphone Texts
Obsessed with texting friends or family about every mundane thing you do throughout the day ☐

Smartphone Selfies
Obsessed with taking location selfies, glamour selfies, and selfies with friends or family ☐

Smartphone Pictures
Obsessed with taking pictures of everyone and everything ☐

Smartphone News
Obsessed with reading/watching the news all day long ☐

Smartphone Videos
Obsessed with watching YouTube or Netflix whenever a single free moment arises ☐

TV
Obsessed with having the TV on day and night as background noise and comfort ☐

Audio Media
Obsessed with listening to the radio, Spotify, Audible books, or podcasts while cleaning, driving, or putzing around the house

Snacks
Obsessed with constant snacking throughout the day

Food
Obsessed with food, food preparation, food shopping, food picture taking, food discussion

Alcohol
You can't get through the evening without your 5pm glass of whiskey, wine, or beer

Cigarettes
You need a hit of nicotine to relax and be in the present moment.

Porn
You turn on the computer and masturbate to porn before doing anything else.

Talking-Gabbing
You talk and talk and talk but hardly ever listen.

I get a lot of comments about the ending of chapter four in *Spirituality for Badasses Book 1*, where I ask you to delete the social media apps from your phone. Many people find it funny or odd that I have a Facebook account... "Hey—you have Facebook! You told us to delete Facebook!"

This dances around a great point, and it's the heart of what the book is about. My response is this: Yes, I do have Facebook. It's on my computer, in the office, waaaaay down in the basement of my home. It's not on my phone. I get zero social media notifications on my phone. My wife, son, mother, sister, and a handful of close friends can call or text me on my phone. That's it.

Here's the heart of the matter: By strictly limiting what's on my phone, I've created a space...a personal no-fly zone around J. Stewart...a buffer where I am free to do whatever the fuck I want to do and be whatever the fuck I want to be...with no interruptions or distractions from my phone.

Spirituality for Badasses is all about removing shit that impedes your personal space. Most of us need to remove a bunch of shit in order to heal our unhappy, depressed, and anxious hearts. Your heart truly longs to be free. You accommodate it by creating space—both externally and internally. Doesn't matter where you start or how you do it, but space must be cultivated and maintained.

Spiritual Badass Homework:

Take the distractions you checked off in the list above seriously. They're draining your time, energy, and life. You don't need them. You're a badass.

- Take the most often occurring and worst distraction from your list and go without it for a *day.*
- Next, go without it for a *week.*
- And then, go without it for a *month.*
- After that, assess whether or not you really need that distraction ever again.

Why do this?

You're addicted to distractions. By removing them, you gain time, energy, space, and freedom. By removing them—you empower your inner spiritual badass.

LESSON 6
THE NIGHT SKY

How to ask & answer the BIG questions

How do you get the audio files? To access the audio files that complement and complete this workbook, go to the back of this workbook (page 281) where you'll find a web address. Go to the web address, follow the instructions there and create an account. If you prefer video there's an option to upgrade.

Notes:

LESSON 7
YOUR EMOTIONAL BRAIN

How to be emotionally intelligent

Originally published in 2005, Daniel Goleman's highly acclaimed book *Emotional Intelligence: Why It Can Matter More Than IQ* redefined *smart*. His argument was straightforward: Intelligence is more than IQ, intellect, memory, or academic prowess. Emotional intelligence is the capacity to be aware of, control, and express one's emotions, skillfully and without drama.

My own personal journey was never defined by intellect. I knew I was smart, but not in the usual way. The spiritual badass journey makes one *well-rounded* smart. I know, I know—I use some fancy words from time to time but, generally speaking, I'm like most guys. Give me a beer and a fishing pole and I'm happy…or I should say…I'm existentially at peace and am able to express my inner drunken joy.

So—let's help you discover the full range of *your* emotional intelligence. It begins, simply enough, by placing your attention on emotions. If your attention has been avoiding, running from, or numbing over certain emotions, this exercise will help you to stop doing so. We want your attention to have honesty, clarity, and integrity regarding *all* your emotions. We are not judging, comparing, or assigning meaning to emotions. We are merely paying attention to them. Here we go…

Attention on Emotions Exercise:

Time required: 10-15 Minutes

Preparation: Find a comfortable quiet space where you won't be disturbed. It's best to sit in a relaxed, comfortable position as you read and check off the boxes that apply.

Task: 1-10 Scale. Read through the list of emotions below and rate on a scale of 1-10, by placing a number in the box, how often you experience the emotion.

Breathe: Begin by taking three deep breaths so that your answers come from *both* body and mind.

Emotions

Peace?
Do you have feelings of peace? How often do you have feelings of peace? ☐

Joy?
Do you have feelings of joy? How often do you have feelings of joy? ☐

Ecstasy?
Do you have feelings of ecstasy? How often do you have feelings of ecstasy? ☐

Trust?
Do you have feelings of trust? How often do you have feelings of trust? ☐

Admiration?
Do you have feelings of admiration? How often do you have feelings of admiration? ☐

Love?
Do you have feelings of love? How often do you have feelings of love? ☐

Apprehension?
Do you have feelings of apprehension? How often do you have feelings of apprehension? ☐

Fear?
Do you have feelings of fear? How often do you have feelings of fear?

Terror?
Do you have feelings of terror? How often do you have feelings of terror?

Distraction?
Do you have feelings of distraction? How often do you have feelings of distraction?

Surprise?
Do you have feelings of surprise? How often do you have feelings of surprise?

Amazement?
Do you have feelings of amazement? How often do you have feelings of amazement?

Pensiveness?
Do you have feelings of pensiveness? How often do you have feelings of pensiveness?

Sadness?
Do you have feelings of sadness? How often do you have feelings of sadness?

Grief?
Do you have feelings of grief? How often do you have feelings of grief?

Boredom?
Do you have feelings of boredom? How often do you have feelings of boredom?

Disgust?
Do you have feelings of disgust? How often do you have feelings of disgust?

Loathing?
Do you have feelings of loathing? How often do you have feelings of loathing?

Annoyance?
Do you have feelings of annoyance? How often do you have feelings of annoyance?

Anger?
Do you have feelings of anger? How often do you have feelings of anger?

Rage?
Do you have feelings of rage? How often do you have feelings of rage?

Emotional Opposites

Acceptance?
Do you have feelings of acceptance? How often do you have feelings of acceptance?

Guilt?
Do you have feelings of guilt? How often do you have feelings of guilt?

Elation?
Do you have feelings of elation? How often do you have feelings of elation?

Depression?
Do you have feelings of depression? How often do you have feelings of depression?

Superiority?
Do you have feelings of superiority? How often do you have feelings of superiority?

Unworthiness?
Do you have feelings of unworthiness? How often do you have feelings of unworthiness?

Confidence?
Do you have feelings of confidence? How often do you have feelings of confidence?

Shame?
Do you have feelings of shame? How often do you have feelings of shame?

Humility?
Do you have feelings of humility? How often do you have feelings of humility?

Boastfulness?
Do you have feelings of boastfulness? How often do you have feelings of boastfulness?

Balance?
Do you have feelings of balance? How often do you have feelings of balance?

Exhaustion?
Do you have feelings of exhaustion? How often do you have feelings of exhaustion?

Loved?
Do you have feelings of being loved? How often do you have feelings of being loved?

Unloved?
Do you have feelings of being unloved? How often do you have feelings of being unloved?

Sexual?
Do you have feelings of being sexual? How often do you have feelings of being sexual?

Asexual?
Do you have feelings of being asexual? How often do you have feelings of being asexual?

Heard and Seen?

Do you have feelings of being heard and seen? How often do you have feelings of being heard and seen?

Not Heard and Seen?

Do you have feelings of not being heard and seen? How often do you have feelings of not being heard and seen?

Alone or Aloof?

Do you have feelings of being alone or aloof? How often do you have feelings of being alone or aloof?

Outgoing and Social?

Do you have feelings of being outgoing and social? How often do you have feelings of being outgoing and social?

Intellectual?

Do you have feelings of being intellectual? How often do you have feelings of being intellectual?

Ignorant?

Do you have feelings of being ignorant? How often do you have feelings of being ignorant?

Spiritual?

Do you have feelings of being spiritual? How often do you have feelings of being spiritual?

Material?

Do you have feelings of being material? How often do you have feelings of being material?

Spiritual Badass Homework:

Like most of us, you're probably avoiding some emotions and overindulging in others. The low-numbered emotions are more than likely the ones you avoid. The high-numbered emotions are the ones you probably use like a pro. There's no wrong or right here. There's just seeing and accepting your full emotional range. Some suggestions...

- Give yourself permission to experience the emotions you avoid. Risk it. Go outside your comfort zone. Yes! Get angry, cry, or laugh!!!
- Watch yourself the next time you instantly react with your favorite go-to emotions. Are you on auto-pilot?
- Pay *attention* to your emotions.
- Emotions are your paints. Why paint in black and white only? Use all your colors!

Why do this?

Your full emotional range is neither good nor bad. It's a color palate. The more you begin to pay attention to your emotions, the more color choice you experience. The more color choice you experience, the easier it is to "paint" an emotional picture of your life which is more nuanced, subtle, beautiful, easier, and nicer.

Notes:

LESSON 8
YOUR THOUGHTS AREN'T ORIGINAL

How to separate yourself from your thoughts

S orry to dash your hopes of becoming a brilliant original thinker, but, my beautiful badass friend, the thoughts in your head aren't any different than the thoughts in the heads of the other seven billion people who live on our lonely little planet. And, even worse, 99% of the thoughts you do have are being replayed on an hourly-daily loop like a bad disco song lingering in your brain days after you've heard it.

Ouch, sorry if that hurt, but get it over it. You are *way* more than the thoughts in your head. You are way more amazing, beautiful, awesome, mysterious, ineffable, and precious than those silly thoughts in your head.

In Michael A Singer's renowned book *The Untethered Soul* he says this on page three of chapter one: "*There is nothing more important to true spiritual growth than realizing that you are not the voice of the mind–you are the one who hears it.*"

I couldn't agree more.

Attention on Thoughts Exercise:

Time required: 10-15 Minutes

Preparation: Find a comfortable quiet space where you won't be disturbed. It's best to sit in a relaxed, comfortable position as you read and check off the boxes that apply.

Task: Read through the list of thoughts below and check the boxes of the ones that most apply to you.

Breathe: Begin by taking three deep breaths so that your answers come from *both* body and mind.

Common Negative Thoughts

I'm not there yet.	☐
When I get this, I'll be...	☐
I'll be happy when...	☐
I hope I get the...	☐
I can't do it.	☐
I can't get it right.	☐
I'm a failure.	☐
I'm not successful.	☐
I'll never understand.	☐
It'll never happen to me.	☐
I'm not good enough.	☐
I'm not smart enough.	☐
I'm too old.	☐
I'm too young.	☐
I don't have enough...	☐
I'm not rich.	☐
I'm not pretty.	☐
I'm too heavy.	☐
I don't feel like	☐

I wasn't born with

I'm not talented enough

My life sucks.

I hate life.

Why does life have to be so

Why me, God?

Bullshit.

Fuck you.

Fuck me.

Fuck everything.

Fuck this place.

This is hell.

What a shit hole.

God damn it.

Are you fucking kidding me?

There's not enough time.

Why is this taking so long?

I'll be here forever.

I'm not there yet.

When I get _____then I'll be ...

I'll be happy when...

I don't want to go to ...

I hate this ...

I'm damaged.

I'm depressed.

I'm sad.

I'm lonely.

I'm empty.

I'm unhappy.

I'm afraid.

I'm pissed off.

Common Positive Thoughts

Oh man that was ...

Wow that was...

What fun that...

What a beautiful...

It was an amazing...

I'm very grateful ...

Thank you so much!...

I'm very fond of...

She's so very...

He's so very...

I like ...

I love...

I'm excited for...

Delicious...

Awesome! I get a ...

I'm capable of...

I can do ...

I got this.

I want to try...

Sign me up.

I'm not afraid of ...

Common Thought Patterns

Reading Minds
He thinks I'm a loser. She hates me.

Predicting the future
I'll fail that exam. I won't get that job.

Catastrophizing
I won't be able to pay the mortgage. We'll be out on the street.

Negative labeling
I'm undesirable. He's a rotten person.

Discounting positives
Those successes were easy, so they don't matter. She's supposed to cook dinner.

Seeing only negative
No one likes me. Another crappy day...

Overgeneralizing
This always happens to me. I fail at everything.

Exaggeration
Everyone rejects me. It was a big waste of time.

Shoulds
I should do well; if I don't, then I'm a failure. I should get a raise.

Personalization
My marriage ended because I failed.

Blame
She's to blame for the way I feel now. My parents caused all my problems.

Comparison
She's more successful than I am. He's better looking than me.

Regret
I could have won if only I'd tried harder. I shouldn't have said that.

What if
What if I make a mistake? What if I'm not good enough?

Victim
There's nothing I can do to change it. We're just pawns in their...

Judgment
He's smarter than me. She's successful. I'm not.

You're responsible
It's my fault you're not happy. I can make you happy and a better person.

You see fairly
I see what is reasonable and fair and you don't.

Change others
If I can just get her to change, she'll be happy.

Always right
I know I'm right and I'll prove it to them.

Fantasy Rewards
After all this hard work, I deserve recognition, success, reward. Why the hell wasn't I rewarded after all that hard work?

Spiritual Badass Homework:

The sooner you realize that you are not the thoughts in your head, the better. You're the *observer* of the thoughts. Thoughts come and go constantly. The only way to gain distance from thoughts is to start paying attention to them. Grab your journal:

- Write down your top three negative thoughts.
- Write down your top three positive thoughts.
- Write down your top three thought patterns.

Why do this?

They're just thoughts. But most people don't think so. Wedge some space between your thoughts and the real you (again, the *observer* of the thoughts) and amazing things will happen.

.

Notes:

LESSON 9
BODY ATTENTION

How to relax your flawed body

W e're going to upgrade your experience options here in Lesson 9. You can read it, share it with a friend, or listen to the audio. My advice: If it's *just you*, definitely listen to the audio. It's easier. You'll relax more. You'll get more out of it. Second best would be if you share the exercise with a friend or relative. They can read it while you are relaxing, and then you can swap. If you're a teacher or guide, you can read this in class.

Body Attention Exercise:

Time required: 15-20 Minutes

Preparation: Find a comfortable quiet space where you won't be disturbed. It's best to sit in a relaxed, comfortable position as you read, listen, or watch.

Task: Below is the script for reading and sharing *The Body Attention Exercise*. You can use it to do a self-guided reading (without the use of the online audio or video) or you can get together with a friend or relative and share it. If you are a teacher or guide, you can read this script in class.

Three Deep Breaths: Begin by taking three deep breaths so that you learn with *both* body and mind.

1. Take a large inhale followed by a large exhale.
2. Take a second large inhale followed by a large exhale.
3. Take a third large inhale followed by a large exhale.

Briefly tune in to the current state of the body:
Pay attention to the general state of the body—tired, achy, hungry, relaxed, excited, hopeful, agitated, nervous, concerned, or perhaps not feeling much of anything. Allow everything to be as it is.

Basic Breathing Body Relaxation:
Read the following slowly, breathe when asked, and notice each body part for a few seconds:

1. Place your attention on your toes, your feet, and your ankles. Breathe…
2. Place your attention on your shins, calves, knees, and your thighs. Breathe…
3. Place your attention on your thighs—where they connect to your knees, the middle, and where they connect to your hips. Breathe…
4. Place your attention on your pelvis, genitals, and bottom. Breathe…
5. Place your attention on your abdomen, belly, belly button, lower back, and lower spinal cord. Breathe…
6. Place your attention on your chest, your heart, your upper back. Breathe…
7. Place your attention on your shoulders, arms, elbows, hands, and fingers. Breathe…
8. Place your attention on your neck, face, forehead, scalp, and top of your head. Breathe…
9. Lastly, place your attention on your entire body. Breathe...

Task Continued & Questions for your body:
After getting in a relaxed state, read the body questions on pages 82-83 and check those that apply.

How do you get the audio files? To access the audio files that complement and complete this workbook, go to the back of this workbook (page 281) where you'll find a web address. Go to the web address, follow the instructions there and create an account. If you prefer video there's an option to upgrade.

Listen to audio and you'll be guided to check the boxes here:

Is your body healthy?	☐
Is your body receiving proper nutrition?	☐
Is your body receiving enough exercise?	☐
Is your body feeling good?	☐
Is your body feeling bad?	☐
Is your body young?	☐
Is your body old?	☐
Is your body ill?	☐
Is your body damaged?	☐
Is your body in need of repair?	☐
Is your body working properly?	☐
Is your body overweight?	☐
Is your body underweight?	☐
Is your body skinny?	☐
Is your body weak?	☐
Is your body strong?	☐
Is your body constantly exhausted?	☐
Is your body full of energy?	☐
Is your body in any pain?	☐
Is your body feeling pleasure?	☐
Is your body stressed?	☐

Is your body at peace? ☐

Is your body irritated? ☐

Is your body hot or cold? ☐

Is your body achy? ☐

Is your body contracted? ☐

Is your body agitated? ☐

Is your body restless? ☐

Is your body always fidgeting? ☐

Is your body comfortable in its own skin? ☐

Is your body accepted? ☐

Is your body rejected? ☐

Is your body ugly? ☐

Is your body beautiful? ☐

Is your body hated? ☐

Is your body loved? ☐

ATTENTION LETTER

Handwrite Me a Letter

Handwrite me a letter about your experience with *Spirituality for Badasses The Workbook Part One: Attention Lessons*. No– I don't want to be your pen pal, but I do want you to practice writing and journaling. *Your letter will be 100% private and not shared.* I've provided a list of questions below. You can use the questions as a guide, or write whatever moves you.

Why do this?

Writing out your deepest thoughts, fears, confessions, and internal dialogues will be very helpful for your spiritual badass journey. *It will get you there quicker.* Writing, sharing, or confessing *to someone* gets it out of *you* and into the light of day, where it can heal, transform, and benefit. Also—writing by hand is better. We tend to be more honest with a pen in hand.

Attention Letter Questions:

- Why are you here? (Reading this book)
- What's your best badass trait?
- What do you lie about most often?
- What do you deny most often?
- What distracts you the most?
- What is your biggest emotional button?
- What thought do you repeat the most?
- How's your relationship to your body?

Send it here:

PIE Publishing c/o J. Stewart Dixon
P.O. Box 32
Earlysville VA 22936

Notes:

END PART 1

After you've completed *The Workbook* continue
your adventure with author J. Stewart Dixon.
Get Access to:
New Book Sneak Previews,
Online Courses, Videos, Humor,
Spiritual Badass Wisdom &
Swear Words for all.

Go here:
www.spiritualityforbadasses.com

PART 2

Awareness Lessons

LESSON 10
EVOLUTIONARY REFRESHER COURSE

*How to be more aware and
evolve the lack*

How ya doin', sunshine?

Just checking in with you.

You aren't trying to cram all these lessons and exercises into one weekend, are you? I'd advise against that. You'll burn yourself out like a blowtorch on a stick of incense.

Take it slow. No rush. If days or weeks go by between lessons—that's okay.

That said, you probably don't want to take a year either. I'm thinking around eight to ten weeks is a good time frame to read and engage with this workbook. Do one lesson every few days. Something like that. Just keep a steady pace and you'll start to notice real and awesome changes.

Coolness. Let's keep going…

Welcome to Part Two of *The Workbook: Awareness Lessons.* In this part you're going to learn how to recognize awareness, get in touch with it more, integrate it deeply into your day-to-day life—and finally experience its positive, beneficial effects.

But—I'm also an evil-genius taskmaster and am going to add another required lesson in this part: You're going to learn how to become more aware of your particular existential yearning or lack.

Here's a refresher regarding awareness:

"The relationship between attention and awareness is like an arrow. Attention (which you *already* have) is the pointed end of the arrow and *awareness* (which you *also already* have) is the fletching—the feathered end of the arrow. You can't really separate the two, but they can indeed and quite often do become out of balance.

Most people are clueless—out of balance—regarding the full potential of awareness: It's usually unnoticed, taken for granted, or conceived of as just a small part of the functioning brain. But snoop around a bit, and you'll discover that awareness is pretty damn amazing and a lot more important than you would ever have expected."

Here's a refresher regarding existential yearning or lack:

"Existential yearning is none other than the natural force of evolution itself. It can be subtle, presenting itself in the form of curiosity, questioning, or doubting. Or it can be severe, presenting itself in the form of pain, suffering, depression, or meaninglessness. Either way, it's usually experienced as a lack or a hole or a missing of something."

Here's a refresher regarding how the two work together:

"The counterintuitive paradoxical badass solution to lack is this:

You ready?

You can't kill the lack.

You can notice it. You can pay attention to it. You can accept it. You can embrace it. You can even love it if you want to. But you cannot kill it, get rid of it, or eliminate it. Never, ever.

You can only do what evolution is asking you to do: Become *aware* of the lack and *evolve* it. This whole book and the road trip adventure we're taking together *is all about evolving your lack—with awareness.*"

Finally, here's a refresher regarding evolution's invitation:

"Over time, I came to see my own existential yearning *manifested as depression*—not as a flaw to be drugged or numbed, but as an invitation from evolution itself:

Wake up, Dumbass...you're still in a cocoon! No wonder you're unhappy. It's dark and cramped in there. Get the hell out of that thing!

Giving my attention to and accepting this evolutionary invitation was one of the best decisions I've ever made. It ended my depression and it fulfilled the yearning."

Awesome...

Now it's your turn to *experience* all this.

Eh...no. Come on now, stop it. (I can feel your anxious squirming) Don't get overwhelmed...

I got ya covered, baby.

We're going to take this *one small step* at a time.

I'm going to make it simple for you.

I'm going to make it doable for you.

Alright? Take a deep breath...

Now you're ready...

You're going to answer evolution's invitation—

by evolving your particular lack—

with awareness.

You got this.

Some things you'll need during Part Two:

- A scented candle or stick of incense
- An orange (or any fruit will do, really)
- A place to stand and do a few bodily movement exercises
- A device to listen to audio or watch some videos

Spiritual Badass Homework:

Transforming what you perceive as a fault, flaw, or problem into a personal invitation from the universe to change, grow, and evolve is some powerful mojo. In the next lesson we're going to dive deep into this, but I'm betting you have a pretty good idea of what your invitation is already. Grab your journal and write it out:

- What's your invitation?
- How does it show up?
- Do you embrace it or fight it?

Why do this?

The more we become of aware of our invitation, the more we can respond to it—and then make the necessary changes.

Notes:

LESSON 11
EVOLUTION'S INVITATION

How to be aware of your invitation

Listen

I'm not going to tell you how to access the audio files from here on out. You should already have access. But, because I'm a nice spiritual badass guy, one last time:

How do you get the audio files? To access the audio files that complement and complete this workbook, go to the back of this workbook (page 281) where you'll find a web address. Go to the web address, follow the instructions there and create an account. If you prefer video there's an option to upgrade.

Evolution's Invitation Exercise:

Time required: 15-20 Minutes

Preparation: Find a comfortable quiet space where you won't be disturbed. It's best to sit in a relaxed, comfortable position.

Task: Listen to the audio, *Lesson 11- Evolution's Invitation* and check the boxes that most apply to you.

Breathe: Begin by taking three deep breaths so that your answers come from *both* body and mind.

Listen to audio and you'll be guided to check and answer here:

Unhappy	☐
Depressed	☐
Anxious	☐
Unloved	☐
Don't love yourself	☐
Don't like yourself	☐
Hate yourself	☐
Hate life	☐
Lonely	☐
Angry	☐
Frustrated	☐
Something is missing	☐
Life isn't good enough	☐

Lost, clueless

Don't fit in

Born on wrong planet

Square peg, round hole

Isolated

Separate

No joy

Blue all the time

There's got to be something more to life

Hole in heart

Untethered, ungrounded

No self-confidence

Emotionally wounded, broken

Abused

Bored

Go through life half-hearted and disinterested

Pessimistic

Skeptical

Jaded

No hope

Life is suffering

On a scale of 1-10, how loud is your invitation?

Where in your body do you usually feel your invitation?:
Answer:

_____

What emotions does your invitation usually elicit?
Short word or two answer:

_____

What thoughts does your invitation usually elicit?
Short word or two answer:

_____

On a scale of 1-10, how reluctant are you to answer your
invitation?

On a scale of 1-10, how likely are you to accept your
invitation?

On a scale of 1-10, how much does the nagging sense of
your invitation affect your life?

How many times per day do you hear your invitation?

How many times per month do you hear your invitation?

How many times per year do you hear your invitation?

Are you okay knowing that your invitation will never go
away? Circle one: YES / NO

Are you okay knowing that the only way to deal with your
invitation is to become intimately *aware* of it?
Circle one: YES / NO

Are you okay knowing that your invitation is actually a gift,
and not a problem or flaw?
Circle one: YES / NO

Now that you've done the exercise, let's see if you've discovered anything new about your invitation. Grab your journal and write down anything and everything you can think of about your invitation. What is your invitation? How is it showing up? Write stream of consciousness style: Don't think about it. Just scribble, scrawl and let-er-rip. Don't worry about grammar, punctuation or even your ability to reread it. Let it all out. Yell at your invitation. Love it. Curse it. Don't hold back.

Why do this?

It's good practice to get all that internal shit out. You've probably never thought about your personal invitation like you have here. It's good to bring it *all* out into the light of day— good or bad.

Notes:

LESSON 12
CANDLES & BROOMSTICKS

How to be aware while seeing & smelling

G rab a scented candle or stick of incense, eye of newt, wing of bat, and your favorite broomstick. Let's get witchy. Just kidding—everyone knows bat wings taste terrible.

Awareness Sight & Smell Exercise:

Time required: 20-30 minutes

Preparation: Find a comfortable quiet space where you won't be disturbed. It's best to sit in a relaxed, comfortable position as you read, listen, or watch.

Task: Below is the script for reading and sharing *The Awareness in Sight and Smell Exercise.* You can read this to yourself, listen to the audio or get together with a friend or relative and share it. If you are a teacher or guide, you can read the script to your class.

Three Deep Breaths: Begin by taking three deep breaths so that you learn with *both* body and mind.

1. Take a large inhale followed by a large exhale.
2. Take a second large inhale followed by a large exhale.
3. Take a third large inhale followed by a large exhale.

Briefly tune in to the current state of the body:
Pay attention to the general state of the body—tired, achy, hungry, relaxed, excited, hopeful, agitated, nervous, concerned, or perhaps not feeling much of anything. Allow everything to

be as it is.

Basic Breathing Body Relaxation:
Read the following slowly, breathe when asked, and notice each body part for a few seconds:

1. Place your attention on your toes, your feet, and your ankles. Breathe…
2. Place your attention on your shins, calves, knees, and your thighs. Breathe…
3. Place your attention on your thighs—where they connect to your knees, the middle, and where they connect to your hips. Breathe…
4. Place your attention on your pelvis, genitals, and bottom. Breathe…
5. Place your attention on your abdomen, belly, belly button, lower back, and lower spinal cord. Breathe…
6. Place your attention on your chest, your heart, your upper back. Breathe…
7. Place your attention on your shoulders, arms, elbows, hands, and fingers. Breathe…
8. Place your attention on your neck, face, forehead, scalp, and the top of your head. Breathe…
9. Lastly, place your attention on your entire body. Breathe...

Okay—let's light the candle. (Please don't burn your house down.)

Take another deep breath:

- Place your attention on what the candle looks like.
- Notice its shape, color, movement, flickering flame, undulating smoke.
- Now notice…**the act of**...seeing the candle.
- While you are seeing the candle, notice you are aware that you are seeing it.
- Here's the really important part:

- Being *aware* that you are seeing the candle and not merely *seeing* it...is to recognize awareness.
- I will say it again: **Being *aware* that you are seeing the candle** and not merely seeing it...is to recognize awareness.
- Notice again that you are *aware* of seeing the candle.

Take another deep breath:

- Now...place your attention on what the candle smells like.
- Notice if it is strong, weak, harsh, flowery, sweet, pungent.
- Now notice... **the act of**...smelling the candle.
- While you are smelling the candle, notice you are *aware* that you are smelling it.
- Here's the really important part: Being aware that you are smelling the candle and not merely smelling it...is to recognize awareness.
- I will say it again: **Being *aware* that you are smelling the candle** and not merely smelling it...is to recognize awareness.
- Notice again that you are *aware* of smelling the candle.

LESSON 13
ORANGES & BATWINGS

How to be aware while touching & tasting

G rab that orange (or any piece of fruit) and let's swallow it whole. Kidding—*don't* swallow it whole. Big waste of an orange.

Awareness Touch & Taste Exercise:

Time required: 20-30 minutes

Preparation: Find a comfortable quiet space where you won't be disturbed. It's best to sit in a relaxed, comfortable position as you read, listen, or watch.

Task: Below is the script for reading and sharing *The Awareness in Touch and Taste Exercise.* You can read this to yourself, listen to the audio or get together with a friend or relative and share it. If you are a teacher or guide, you can read the script in class.

Three Deep Breaths: Begin by taking three deep breaths so that you learn with *both* body and mind.

1. Take a large inhale followed by a large exhale.
2. Take a second large inhale followed by a large exhale.
3. Take a third large inhale followed by a large exhale.

Briefly tune in to the current state of the body:
Pay attention to the general state of the body—tired, achy, hungry, relaxed, excited, hopeful, agitated, nervous, concerned, or perhaps not feeling much of anything. Allow everything to

be as it is.

Basic Breathing Body Relaxation:
Read the following slowly, breathe when asked, and notice each body part for a few seconds:

1. Place your attention on your toes, your feet, and your ankles. Breathe...
2. Place your attention on your shins, calves, knees, and your thighs. Breathe...
3. Place your attention on your thighs—where they connect to your knees, the middle, and where they connect to your hips. Breathe...
4. Place your attention on your pelvis, genitals, and bottom. Breathe...
5. Place your attention on your abdomen, belly, belly button, lower back, and lower spinal cord. Breathe...
6. Place your attention on your chest, your heart, your upper back. Breathe...
7. Place your attention on your shoulders, arms, elbows, hands, and fingers. Breathe...
8. Place your attention on your neck, face, forehead, scalp, and the top of your head. Breathe...
9. Lastly, place your attention on your entire body. Breathe...

Okay, now grab that orange (or banana, grape, or strawberry). Leave the bat wing and eye of newt in the cupboard.

Take a deep breath:

- Place the orange in your hand.
- Place your attention on what the orange feels like to the touch.
- Squeeze it slightly. Roll it between your palms. Rub it with a finger.

- Notice if it's rough, smooth, dry, wet, hot, cold, slippery, craggy...
- Now notice...**the act of**...touching the orange.
- While you are touching the orange, notice you are *aware* that you are touching it.
- Here's the really important part: Being *aware* that you are touching the orange and not merely touching it...is to recognize awareness.
- I will say it again: **Being *aware* that you are touching the orange** and not merely touching it...is to recognize awareness.
- Notice again that you are *aware* of touching the orange.

Take another deep breath:

- Now...take a piece of the orange (Obviously, you need to peel it first.), place it in your mouth, and slowly begin to chew it.
- Place your attention on what the orange tastes like.
- Notice if it's sweet, sour, bland...
- Now notice...**the act of**...tasting the orange.
- While you are tasting the orange, notice you are *aware* that you are tasting it.
- Here's the really important part: Being *aware* that you are tasting the orange and not merely tasting it...is to recognize awareness.
- I will say it again: **Being *aware* that you are tasting the orange** and not merely tasting it...is to recognize awareness.
- Notice again that you are *aware* of tasting the orange.

Notes:

Notes:

LESSON 14
SONIC BOOMS & TIBETAN BELLS

How to be aware while hearing & listening

O kay. You'll need something that makes a sound for this exercise. A spoon and a glass will work, and so will a fighter jet engine if you have one of those lying around. If you listen to the audio or watch the video version of this exercise, I'll be using a cool little Tibetan bowl chime thingy.

Awareness Hear & Listen Exercise:

Time required: 20-30 minutes

Preparation: Find a comfortable quiet space where you won't be disturbed. It's best to sit in a relaxed, comfortable position as you read, listen, or watch.

Task: Below is the script for reading and sharing *The Awareness in Hearing Exercise*. You can read this to yourself, listen to the audio or get together with a friend or relative and share it. If you are a teacher or guide, you can read the script in class.

Three Deep Breaths: Begin by taking three deep breaths so that you learn with *both* body and mind.

1. Take a large inhale followed by a large exhale.
2. Take a second large inhale followed by a large exhale.
3. Take a third large inhale followed by a large exhale.

Briefly tune in to the current state of the body:
Pay attention to the general state of the body—tired, achy, hungry, relaxed, excited, hopeful, agitated, nervous, concerned,

111

or perhaps not feeling much of anything. Allow everything to be as it is.

Basic Breathing Body Relaxation:
Read the following slowly, breathe when asked, and notice each body part for a few seconds:

1. Place your attention on your toes, your feet, and your ankles. Breathe...
2. Place your attention on your shins, calves, knees, and your thighs. Breathe...
3. Place your attention on your thighs—where they connect to your knees, the middle, and where they connect to your hips. Breathe...
4. Place your attention on your pelvis, genitals, and bottom. Breathe...
5. Place your attention on your abdomen, belly, belly button, lower back, and lower spinal cord. Breathe...
6. Place your attention on your chest, your heart, your upper back. Breathe...
7. Place your attention on your shoulders, arms, elbows, hands, and fingers. Breathe...
8. Place your attention on your neck, face, forehead, scalp, and the top of your head. Breathe...
9. Lastly, place your attention on your entire body. Breathe...

Okay—grab your chime, glass, or jet engine. In this exercise, you'll practice the art of hearing awareness.

Take a deep breath...

- Tap the chime.
- Notice the tone, pitch, depth, and duration of its sound.
- Now notice...**the act of**...hearing the chime.
- While you are hearing the chime, notice you are *aware* that you are hearing it.

- Here's the really important part: **Being *aware* that you are hearing** the chime and not merely hearing it...is to recognize awareness.
- Notice again that you are *aware* of hearing the chime.

Now let's do the same with the sound of my voice. In this exercise, you'll practice the art of listening awareness. Listening is slightly different than hearing. With listening, you're also processing meaning and information through words or language.

Take a deep breath...

- Listen to the sound of my voice.
- Notice the tone, pitch, depth, and duration of my voice.
- Notice that you are processing meaning and information through listening.
- Now notice...**the act of**...listening to my voice.
- While you are listening to my voice, notice you are *aware* that you are listening.
- Here's the really important part: **Being *aware* that you are listening** to my voice and not merely listening to it...is to recognize awareness.
- Notice again that you are *aware* of listening.

Lesson 14:
Sonic Booms & Tibetan Bells

Listen

LESSON 15
MOVING & BREAK DANCING

How to be aware while moving your body

"Let's dance. Put on your red shoes and dance the blues.
Let's dance. To the song they're playin' on the radio.
Let's sway. While color lights up your face
Let's sway. Sway through the crowd to an empty space."
-David Bowie

Awareness Body Move Exercise:

Time required: 20-30 minutes

Preparation: Find a comfortable quiet space where you won't be disturbed. For the relaxation part, it's best to sit in a relaxed, comfortable position as you read, listen, or watch. For the body movement part, you'll need a space where you can move around a bit.

Task: Below is the script for reading and sharing *The Awareness in Body Movement Exercise*. You can read this to yourself, listen to the audio or get together with a friend or relative and share it. If you are a teacher or guide, you can read the script in class.

Three Deep Breaths: Begin by taking three deep breaths so that you learn with *both* body and mind.

1. Take a large inhale followed by a large exhale.
2. Take a second large inhale followed by a large exhale.
3. Take a third large inhale followed by a large exhale.

Briefly tune in to the current state of the body:
Pay attention to the general state of the body—tired, achy,

115

hungry, relaxed, excited, hopeful,agitated, nervous, concerned, or perhaps not feeling much of anything. Allow everything to be as it is.

Basic Breathing Body Relaxation:
Read the following slowly, breathe when asked, and notice each body part for a few seconds:

1. Place your attention on your toes, your feet, and your ankles. Breathe…
2. Place your attention on your shins, calves, knees, and your thighs. Breathe…
3. Place your attention on your thighs—where they connect to your knees, the middle, and where they connect to your hips. Breathe…
4. Place your attention on your pelvis, genitals, and bottom. Breathe…
5. Place your attention on your abdomen, belly, belly button, lower back, and lower spinal cord. Breathe…
6. Place your attention on your chest, your heart, your upper back. Breathe…
7. Place your attention on your shoulders, arms, elbows, hands, and fingers. Breathe…
8. Place your attention on your neck, face, forehead, scalp, and the top of your head. Breathe…
9. Lastly, place your attention on your entire body. Breathe...

Sitting and Standing Movement: If listening to audio or watching video adjust your device so you can hear or watch it easily.

Take a deep breath…

- Start in the seated position.
- Slowly move from the seated position to the standing position and back to the seated position. Continue doing so, back and forth, until asked to pause.

116

- Place your attention on the bodily movement of sitting and standing. Notice your back movement, muscle clenching, breath, arms, head, feet, muscles, skin, seat, floor...
- Now notice...**the act of**...moving, sitting, and standing.
- While you are moving your body, notice you are *aware* that you are moving it.
- Here's the really important part: **Being *aware* that you are moving your body** and not merely moving it...is to recognize awareness.
- Notice again that you are *aware* of moving your body.
- Pause your movement in the standing position.

Arm Swing Movement: Let's do the same while you swing your arms around.

Take a deep breath...

- Now slowly twist your entire body and swing your arms. With each swing, bring your index finger to the tip of your nose. Keep swinging and touch your nose.
- Place your attention on the bodily movement of arm swinging. Notice your back movement, muscle clenching, breath, arms, head, feet, muscles, skin, seat, floor...
- Now notice...**the act of**...swinging your arms.
- While you are swinging your arms, notice you are *aware* that you are swinging your arms.
- Here's the really important part: **Being *aware* that you are swinging your arms** and not merely swinging them ...is to recognize awareness.
- Notice again that you are *aware* of swinging your arms.

Notes:

Notes:

LESSON 16
PISSED OFF & BLISSED OUT

How to be aware during all emotions

Excellent work, compadre.

Now we 're going to take what you've learned about awareness through the five senses and body movement, and apply it to emotions. Here, the relationship between awareness and emotions is no different. When emotions register (all of them— good, bad, high, low), there is always a silent, witnessing, watching, observing awareness.

If you'll recall, from *Spirituality for Badasses Book 1*, I said this about emotions:

"How we do this has to be a surprise. If I prepared you and told you to get all emotionally worked up about this and that and the other thing, it would just be fake and BS; and as you may have surmised by now, I don't do fake and BS. Badass spirituality goes right for the jugular..."

So—here's how this is going to work: The heart of the exercise in this lesson will be on audio/video. I can easily provide some audio/video- based emotional content that will surprise you. But I'll also provide a basic script here, should you wish to read it with a friend (or in a class). Then you can skip to the audio or video with the emotional exercise in it. Sound good? Cool.

121

Awareness Emotions Exercise:

Time required: 20-30 minutes

Preparation: Find a comfortable quiet space where you won't be disturbed. It's best to sit in a relaxed, comfortable position as you read, listen, or watch.

Task: Below is the script for reading and sharing *The Awareness in Emotion Exercise.* Read the script to familiarize yourself with the exercise, then simply listen to the audio (or watch the video) and follow along. If you are a teacher or guide, you can read the script in class.

Three Deep Breaths: Begin by taking three deep breaths so that you learn with *both* body and mind.

1. Take a large inhale followed by a large exhale.
2. Take a second large inhale followed by a large exhale.
3. Take a third large inhale followed by a large exhale

Briefly tune in to the current state of the body:
Pay attention to the general state of the body—tired, achy, hungry, relaxed, excited, hopeful, agitated, nervous, concerned, or perhaps not feeling much of anything. Allow everything to be as it is.

Basic Breathing Body Relaxation:
Read the following slowly, breathe when asked, and notice each body part for a few seconds:

1. Place your attention on your toes, your feet, and your ankles. Breathe…
2. Place your attention on your shins, calves, knees, and your thighs. Breathe…
3. Place your attention on your thighs—where they connect to your knees, the middle, and where they connect to your hips. Breathe…

122

4. Place your attention on your pelvis, genitals, and bottom. Breathe…
5. Place your attention on your abdomen, belly, belly button, lower back, and lower spinal cord. Breathe…
6. Place your attention on your chest, your heart, your upper back. Breathe…
7. Place your attention on your shoulders, arms, elbows, hands, and fingers. Breathe…
8. Place your attention on your neck, face, forehead, scalp, and the top of your head. Breathe…
9. Lastly, place your attention on your entire body. Breathe…

Positive Emotions.

Take a deep breath…

- In a moment I'm going to play for you an audio/video montage filled with displays of positive emotions.
- **Listen or Watch *Lesson 16: Positive Emotional Exercise***
- While listening/viewing, place your attention on the emotions that arise.
- Feel them, allow them, accept them.
- While you are doing so notice…**the act of**…*emoting*.
- While you are emoting, notice that *you are aware* you are emoting.
- Here's the really important part: **Being *aware* that you are emoting** and not merely emoting…is to recognize awareness.
- Notice again that you are *aware* of emoting.

Negative Emotions.

Take a deep breath...

- In a moment I'm going to play for you a video montage filled with displays of negative emotions.
- **Listen or Watch *Lesson 16: Negative Emotional Exercise***
- While listening/viewing, place your attention on the emotions that arise.
- Feel them, allow them, accept them.
- While you are doing so notice...**the act of**...*emoting.*
- While you are emoting, notice that *you are aware* you are emoting.
- Here's the really important part: **Being *aware* that you are emoting** and not merely emoting...is to recognize awareness.
- Notice again that you are *aware* of emoting.

Lesson 16:
Pissed Off & Blissed Out

Listen

Notes:

LESSON 17
THINK ON THESE THINGS

How to divorce your thoughts

In *Spirituality for Badasses Book 1*, my advice about thoughts goes like this: Divorce them.

"In order to divorce your thoughts, all ya gotta do is insert awareness all the time, every time (no expensive lawyer required). Notice your thoughts. Notice the act of thinking your thoughts. Notice. Notice. Notice. Be aware. Be aware. Be aware. Notice the constant stream of thought BS that pours out of your brain. Do this until you create a space between you and your thoughts so large—so immense and so spacious—that no bridge will ever be able to span it again. No marriage will ever bind and trap those thoughts again."

So, let's begin the formal divorce process. As stated, all you have to do is insert awareness.

Awareness Thoughts Exercise:

Time required: 20-30 minutes

Preparation: Find a comfortable quiet space where you won't be disturbed. It's best to sit in a relaxed, comfortable position as you read, listen, or watch.

Task: Below is the script for reading and sharing *The Awareness in Thought Exercise*. You can read this to yourself, listen to the audio or get together with a friend or relative and share it. If you are a teacher or guide, you can read the script in class.

Three Deep Breaths: Begin by taking three deep breaths so that you learn with *both* body and mind.

1. Take a large inhale followed by a large exhale.
2. Take a second large inhale followed by a large exhale.
3. Take a third large inhale followed by a large exhale.

Briefly tune in to the current state of the body:
Pay attention to the general state of the body—tired, achy, hungry, relaxed, excited, hopeful, agitated, nervous, concerned, or perhaps not feeling much of anything. Allow everything to be as it is.

Basic Breathing Body Relaxation:
Read the following slowly, breathe when asked, and notice each body part for a few seconds:

1. Place your attention on your toes, your feet, and your ankles. Breathe…
2. Place your attention on your shins, calves, knees, and your thighs. Breathe…
3. Place your attention on your thighs—where they connect to your knees, the middle, and where they connect to your hips. Breathe…
4. Place your attention on your pelvis, genitals, and bottom. Breathe…
5. Place your attention on your abdomen, belly, belly button, lower back, and lower spinal cord. Breathe…
6. Place your attention on your chest, your heart, your upper back. Breathe…
7. Place your attention on your shoulders, arms, elbows, hands, and fingers. Breathe…
8. Place your attention on your neck, face, forehead, scalp, and the top of your head. Breathe…
9. Lastly, place your attention on your entire body. Breathe...

Scenario 1 - Specific Thought:

Take a deep breath...

- You just won $500,000. Think about how you will spend half a million dollars. Will you save it or spend it? What will you purchase with it? Who will you help? Where will you travel? Go wild with your thoughts about half a million dollars.
- While you are doing so, notice...**the act of**...*thinking thoughts.*
- While you are thinking, notice that *you are aware* you are thinking.
- Here's the really important part: **Being *aware* that you are thinking** and not merely thinking...is to recognize awareness.
- Notice again that you are *aware* of thinking thoughts.

Scenario 2 - Random Thoughts & Pictures:

Take a deep breath...

- Visualize a rolling green field with a hill and a large tree on it. Think about this scene. Let your thoughts add to this scene in any way you desire—birds, flowers, setting sun, a heard of zebras. Notice your thoughts as you add elements to this scene.
- While you are doing so, notice...**the act of**...*thinking thoughts.*
- While you are thinking, notice that *you are aware* you are thinking.
- Here's the really important part: **Being *aware* that you are thinking** and not merely thinking...is to recognize awareness.
- Notice again that you are *aware* of thinking thoughts.

Scenario 3- Thought Patterns:

Take a deep breath...

- You probably have one or several problems, sore points, or stressors in your life right now. Pick one of these...the biggest, preferably. Think about getting rid of this stressor or relieving yourself of the problem. Notice the usual repeating thought patterns that arise regarding this stressor. (You've probably had these thought patterns many times before.)
- While you are doing so, notice...**the act** of...*thinking thought patterns.*
- While you are thinking, notice that *you are aware* you are thinking thought patterns.
- Here's the really important part: **Being *aware* that you are thinking** and not merely thinking...is to recognize awareness.
- Notice again that you are *aware* of thinking thought patterns.

Lesson 17:
Think On These Things

Listen

Rinse, wash, repeat. I don't need to tell you this, but I will: Pick any one of the previous lessons that you liked and repeat it. Or—if you're feeling especially perky, spunky, or energetic—repeat them all.

Why do this?

This is a spiritual badass gym. The more you visit the gym and sling around the weights, the stronger, wiser, and more badass aware you'll be.

AWARENESS LETTER

Handwrite Me a Letter

Handwrite me a letter about your experience with *The Workbook Part Two- Awareness Lessons. Your letter will be 100% private and not shared.* I've provided a list of questions below you can use as a guide, or write whatever moves you.

Why do this?

Writing out your deepest thoughts, fears, confessions, and internal dialogues will be very helpful for your spiritual badass journey. *It will get you there quicker.* Writing, sharing, or confessing *to someone* gets it out of *you* and into the light of day, where it can heal, transform, and benefit. Also—writing by hand is better. We tend to be more honest with a pen in hand.

Awareness Letter Questions:

- What can you tell me about your existential yearning or lack?
- Is your sense of being aware more defined?
- What do you feel is the hardest thing for you to be aware of?
- What was the hardest awareness exercise for you?
- Have there been any awareness breakthroughs or benefits you can point to?
- What area of your life do you think still needs more awareness?
- How's life?

Send it here:

PIE Publishing c/o J. Stewart Dixon
P.O. Box 32
Earlysville VA 22936

Notes:

Notes:

END PART 2

After you've completed *The Workbook* continue
your adventure with author J. Stewart Dixon.
Get Access to:
New Book Sneak Previews,
Online Courses, Videos, Humor,
Spiritual Badass Wisdom &
Swear Words for all.

Go here:
www.spiritualityforbadasses.com

PART 3

Mindfulness Lessons

LESSON 18
WHAT IS MINDFULNESS?

How to live a mindful life

Welcome to Part Three of *Spirituality for Badasses The Workbook: Mindfulness Lessons.* Before we continue, I have an important message from someone I think you know and love: Lenny! He gives you his best clawed fist-bump, says hi, and can't wait to hang out with you again. I'll give him a back scratch for you!

Here's a refresher regarding mindfulness:

"Mindfulness comes into full focus for an individual when repeated self-observation, attention, and awareness—with complete ease and effortlessness—bring about a spacious, empty, clear, and fundamentally okay internal presence, which has heretofore remained hidden, obscured, or unnoticed.

Getting this mindful part to come into complete focus requires a little effort, practice, and repetition. It's no different than going to the gym. You want mindfulness muscles and all the benefits that come with? You gotta lift some weights and pump some iron.

Imagine four layers, one on top of the other: Mind, Emotion, Body, and Mindful Awareness. Most people live their entire lives with this layered order of magnitude arrangement: Mind out front, hot and bothered, followed by the ups and downs of emotion, then the complications of the body—and finally, mindful awareness in fourth place, lost or buried in the chaos and confusion of the previous three layers.

Spiritual Badasses have equal access to and awareness of all four layers. None are higher or lower, better or worse than the others. And when all are equal, a degree of peaceful equanimity is achieved and purveys throughout. This equanimity is by no means perfect, but it results in a calm bay compared to the usual raging high seas of the person bereft of mindful awareness."

Here's some cool news I think you'll like:

You're already fairly practiced with the fundamentals of a mindfulness exercise. It's simply about paying attention and being aware. *The Basic Breathing Body Relaxation* exercise, where you are asked to notice and relax your whole body from head to toe, is that fundamental. At this point (hopefully) through the reading or audio exercises, you've experienced this gem dozens of times and are accustomed to it.

All we're going to do here in *Part Three: Mindfulness Lessons* is expand upon *The Basic Breathing Body Relaxation* exercise, or "body scan"—as it's known in the MBSR/Mindfulness Based Stress Reduction community. All you have to do is find a comfy bed or yoga mat, lie down, listen, and relax.

A preemptive strike and some proactive advice that will help you deal with the boredom you may experience while doing these exercises:

I'm no fool. I've practiced, taught, and delivered mindfulness exercises hundreds of times. Yes—they can get boring sometimes, so I'm going to do you a solid and try my best to make them slightly more interesting. I've edited into the exercise audio /videos some soothing, unobtrusive, and slightly cheesy background ambiences: things like ocean waves, rain showers, and tropical jungle sounds. My hope is that this will help you overcome any boredom and entice you to repeat the exercises without reluctance or hesitation.

I say "repeat" because mindfulness neuroscience has proven that repeating and practicing the mindfulness body-scan exercise improves results and effectiveness. In other words, if you want to become a Ninja Warrior Jedi Mindfulness Master like Lenny—you'll need to practice more than once.

Some things you'll need during Part Three:

- A bed, yoga mat, or couch to lie on.
- A solid hour of quiet, uninterrupted free time.
- A device to listen to (or watch) the exercises on.

Notes:

LESSON 19
GENERAL BODY SCAN

How to lie down and be mindful

You 've set aside a good hour of quiet, uninterrupted free time. Check. You went out and purchased a brand new $2,000 organic, holistic, holy, and shaman-approved orthopedic mattress stuffed with silk-infused hypoallergenic sheep's wool, complete with a solid oak, hand-carved bed frame. Check. (I sure as hell hope not.) You got your favorite device handy and are ready to hit play. Check. Awesome. You rock.

You're already practiced at the shorter version of the general body scan exercise. Transitioning to this longer, deeper version will be easy for you. Here we go...

The General Body Scan Exercise:

Time required: 30-45 minutes

Preparation: Find a comfortable quiet space where you won't be disturbed. It's best to lie prone on your back in a relaxed, comfortable position as you listen or watch.

Task: Below is the script for reading and sharing *The General Body Scan Exercise*. I do *not* recommend a self-guided reading: You can't read and tune into yourself at the same time. Listen to the audio or watch the video. You can also get together with a friend or relative and share it. If you are a teacher or guide, you can read the script to your class.

Three Deep Breaths: Begin by taking three deep breaths so that you learn with *both* body and mind.

1. Take a large inhale followed by a large exhale.
2. Take second large inhale followed by a large exhale.
3. Take third large inhale followed by a large exhale

Briefly tune into the current state of the body:
Pay attention to the general state of the body—tired, achy, hungry, relaxed, excited, hopeful, agitated, nervous, concerned, or perhaps not feeling much of anything. Allow everything to be as it is.

The Region of Mobility and Balance: Feet, Lower Legs, Knees and Thighs.

- Begin by placing your awareness on the bottom of the LEFT FOOT.
- Move to the HEEL, the ARCH, the BALL and now the TOES.
- Move to the LEFT BIG TOE—the tip, bottom, and top.
- Move to the 5th TOE, the 4th TOE, the 3rd TOE, and now the 2nd TOE.
- Be aware of tips, bottoms, and tops of ALL the TOES.
- Place your awareness on the TOP of the FOOT.
- Move to the ACHILLES TENDON.
- Pause. Now be aware of the ENTIRE LEFT FOOT, including its interior: the blood, bones, and muscles.

Take a moment to notice any thoughts, emotions, or physical sensations. (Reader pause) Allow them to come and go. (Reader pause) Take a slow deliberate breath.

- Next, place your awareness on the LEFT ANKLE.
- Move to the LEFT LOWER LEG—the SHIN and the CALF.
- Move to where the SHIN and CALF connect to the KNEE.
- Move to the LEFT KNEECAP, the sides of the KNEE, the back of the KNEE.

- Move to where the KNEE connects to the THIGH.
- Pause. Now be aware of the entire LOWER LEFT LEG and KNEE, including their interior: the blood, bones, and muscles.

Take a moment to notice any thoughts, emotions, or physical sensations. (Reader pause) Allow them to come and go. (Reader pause) Take a slow deliberate breath.

- Next, place your awareness on the LEFT THIGH, where it connects to the KNEE.
- Move to the MIDDLE THIGH. MOVE to the UPPER THIGH.
- Move to where the UPPER THIGH connects to the HIP.
- Place your awareness on the front, sides and back of the ENTIRE LEFT THIGH.
- Pause. Now be aware of the entire LEFT THIGH,, including its interior: the blood, bones, and muscles.

Take a moment to notice any thoughts, emotions, or physical sensations. (Reader pause) Allow them to come and go. (Reader pause) Take a slow deliberate breath.

- Now place your awareness on the bottom of the RIGHT FOOT.
- Move to the HEEL, the ARCH, the BALL, and now the TOES.
- Move to the RIGHT BIG TOE—the tip, bottom, and top.
- Move to the 5th TOE, the 4th TOE, the 3rd TOE, and now the 2nd TOE.
- Be aware of the tips, bottoms, and tops of ALL the TOES.
- Place your awareness on the TOP of the FOOT.
- Move to the ACHILLES TENDON.
- Pause. Now be aware of the ENTIRE RIGHT FOOT, including its interior: the blood, bones, and muscles.

Take a moment to notice any thoughts, emotions, or physical sensations. (Reader pause) Allow them to come and go. (Reader pause) Take a slow, deliberate breath.

- Next, place your awareness on the RIGHT ANKLE.
- Move to the RIGHT LOWER LEG—the SHIN and the CALF.
- Move to the where the SHIN and CALF connect to the KNEE.
- Move to the RIGHT KNEECAP, the sides of the KNEE, the back of the KNEE.
- Move to where the KNEE connects to the THIGH.
- Pause. Now be aware of the entire LOWER RIGHT LEG and KNEE, including their interior: the blood, bones, and muscles.

Take a moment to notice any thoughts, emotions, or physical sensations. (Reader pause) Allow them to come and go. (Reader pause) Take a slow, deliberate breath.

- Next, place your awareness on the RIGHT THIGH, where it connects to the knee.
- Move to the MIDDLE THIGH. MOVE to the UPPER THIGH. Move to where the UPPER THIGH connects to the HIP.
- Place your awareness on the front, sides, and back of the ENTIRE RIGHT THIGH.
- Pause. Now be aware of the entire RIGHT THIGH,, including its interior: the blood, bones, and muscles.

Take a moment to notice any thoughts, emotions, or physical sensations. (Reader pause) Allow them to come and go. (Reader pause) Take a slow, deliberate breath.

The Region of Reproduction, Digestion, Assimilation, and Elimination: Pelvis, Abdomen, and Lower Back

- Next, place your awareness on the PELVIS, the GENITALS, and the BOTTOM.
- Move to where the THIGHS, BOTTOM, TAILBONE, and GENITALS all meet.
- Next, place your awareness on the ABDOMEN, the BELLY, and the BELLY BUTTON.
- Now place your awareness on the LOWER BACK and LOWER SPINAL CORD.
- Pause. Be aware of the entire PELVIC, ABDOMEN, and LOWER BACK REGION, including the interior: the blood, bones, muscles, and internal organs.

Take a moment to notice any thoughts, emotions, or physical sensations. (Reader pause) Allow them to come and go. (Reader pause) Take a slow, deliberate breath.

The Region of Blood Circulation and Oxygenation: Chest, Heart and Back

- Next, place your awareness on the SOLAR PLEXUS, between the BELLY BUTTON and the HEART.
- Move to the RIBS and STERNUM, the LOWER, MID- and UPPER CHEST, the HEART, the SIDES of the CHEST below the ARMPITS.
- Now place your awareness on the MID BACK and now the UPPER BACK.
- Place your awareness on the lungs. Notice how the entire CHEST REGION inflates and deflates with each breath.
- Pause. Be aware of the entire CHEST, MID BACK, and UPPER BACK REGION, including the interior: the blood, bones, muscles, and internal organs.

Take a moment to notice any thoughts, emotions, or physical sensations. (Reader pause) Allow them to come and go. (Reader pause) Take a slow, deliberate breath.

The Region of Physical Manipulation and Communicative Gesture: Fingers, Hands, and Arms

- Next, place your awareness on the LEFT HAND.
- Place your awareness on the FINGERTIPS, the FINGERS, on the JOINTS in the FINGERS.
- Move to where the FINGERS meet the PALM, the PALM, the BACK of the HAND, the WRIST.
- Move to the LOWER LEFT FOREARM and the upper LEFT FOREARM, and to where they connect to the ELBOW.
- Move to the ELBOW, the UPPER LEFT ARM, the ARMPIT, the area where the UPPER LEFT ARM connects to the SHOULDER.

- Next, place your awareness on the RIGHT HAND.
- Place your awareness on the FINGERTIPS, the FINGERS, the JOINTS.
- Where the FINGERS meet the PALM, the PALM, the BACK of the HAND, the WRIST.
- Move to the LOWER RIGHT FOREARM and the upper RIGHT FOREARM, and to where they connect to the ELBOW.
- Move to the ELBOW, the UPPER RIGHT ARM, the ARMPIT, the area where the UPPER RIGHT ARM connects to the SHOULDER.
- Pause. Be aware of the entirety of both ARMS including their interior: the blood, bones, and muscles of each arm.

Take a moment to notice any thoughts, emotions, or physical sensations. (Reader pause) Allow them to come and go. (Reader pause) Take a slow, deliberate breath.

The Region of Communication, Thought, and Emotion: Shoulders, Face, and Head

- Next, place your awareness on the SHOULDERS, where the SHOULDER MUSCLES slope up to the NECK, the LOWER part of the NECK that connects to the CHEST, the ADAM'S APPLE, the SIDES of the NECK, the BACK of the NECK that connects to the HEAD.
- Next, place your awareness on the JAW, the MOUTH, LIPS, CHEEKS, NOSE, EYES, EYELIDS, TEMPLES, FOREHEAD, EARS.
- Next, place your awareness on the interior cavities of this region.
- The INTERIOR OF THE MOUTH,— TEETH, GUMS, TONGUE, INNER THROAT, TONSILS.
- The NASAL INTERIOR—NOSTRILS and SINUS PASSAGES.
- The EARS—the LEFT LOBE, EXTERIOR CANAL, INNER EAR, the DEEP INNER EAR; the RIGHT LOBE, EXTERIOR CANAL, INNER EAR, the DEEP INNER EAR.
- Next, place your awareness on the TOP of the HEAD, the SCALP, the SKULL, the HAIR, where the HEAD meets the TOP of the NECK.
- Next, place your awareness on the interior cavity of the HEAD and the BRAIN.
- Pause. Be aware of the entire SHOULDER, NECK, FACE, and HEAD REGION, including the interior: the blood, bones, muscles, and organs within.

Take a moment to notice any thoughts, emotions, or physical sensations. (Reader pause) Allow them to come and go. (Reader pause) Take a slow, deliberate breath.

The Entire Body:
Briefly place your awareness on your entire body: Feet, Lower Legs, Knees, Thighs, Pelvis, Abdomen, Lower Back, Chest, Upper Back, Fingers, Hands, Arms, Shoulders, Neck, Face, and Head.

End of The General Body Scan Exercise.
Know that this exercise has your best mindful intention to welcome and integrate all parts of your being—body, awareness, thought, and emotion. Slowly stand up. Move a little and stretch in a gentle way that feels good to you.

Notes:

Obviously, you can't practice the *General Body Scan Exercise* under your desk at work or in the bathroom. But you *can* practice the one below anytime, anyplace. I highly recommend you do so:

The Badass STOP Method:
- **S**top
- **T**ake 30 seconds to place your awareness on your entire body. Take a deep breath first: Feet, Lower legs, Knees, Thighs, Pelvis, Abdomen, Lower Back, Chest, Upper Back, Fingers, Hands, Arms, Shoulders, Neck, Face, and Head.
- **O**bserve your emotions, thoughts, surroundings, and situation.
- **P**roceed.

Why do this?

Because it feels fucking great *and* it will dramatically improve the quality of your day.

LESSON 20
THOUGHT BODY SCAN

How to be mindful of thoughts

You've already placed your attention and awareness on thoughts and thought patterns. Now we'll take a deeper, more mindful look at them.

Mindful awareness has the power to reduce and dissipate the toxic and neurotic effects of repetitive thoughts. Let's be clear here: You ain't gonna eliminate thoughts. That would be impossible. On the contrary, we are seeking to find them, be aware of them, be mindful of them, and ultimately—make peace with them.

Same thing here, champ: one hour of uninterrupted time, a comfy place to lie down, and your favorite device to listen with. Ready, set, go...

The Thought Body Scan Exercise:

Time required: 30-45 minutes

Preparation: Find a comfortable quiet space where you won't be disturbed. It's best to lie prone on your back in a relaxed, comfortable position as you listen or watch.

Task: Below is the script for reading and sharing *The General Body Scan Exercise.* I do *not* recommend a self-guided reading: You can't read and tune into yourself at the same time. Listen to the audio or watch the video. You can also get together with a friend or relative and share it. If you are a teacher or guide, you can read the script to your class.

Three Deep Breaths: Begin by taking three deep breaths so that you learn with *both* body and mind.

1. Take a large inhale followed by a large exhale.
2. Take second large inhale followed by a large exhale.
3. Take third large inhale followed by a large exhale

Briefly tune into the current state of the body:
Pay attention to the general state of the body—tired, achy, hungry, relaxed, excited, hopeful, agitated, nervous, concerned, or perhaps not feeling much of anything. Allow everything to be as it is.

The Region of Mobility and Balance: Feet, Lower Legs, Knees and Thighs

- Begin by placing your awareness on the bottom of the LEFT FOOT.
- Move to the HEEL, the ARCH, the BALL and now the TOES.
- Move to the LEFT BIG TOE—the tip, bottom, and top.
- Move to the 5th TOE, the 4th TOE, the 3rd TOE, and now the 2nd TOE.
- Be aware of tips, bottoms, and tops of ALL the TOES.
- Place your awareness on the TOP of the FOOT.
- Move to the ACHILLES TENDON.
- Pause. Now be aware of the ENTIRE LEFT FOOT, including its interior: the blood, bones, and muscles.

Take a moment to notice any thoughts, emotions, or physical sensations. (Reader pause) Pay particular attention to any recurring thoughts or thought patterns you may be experiencing. Allow these thoughts to come and go, seeing them as a natural part of your mind. Just like the eyes see, the ears hear, and the nose smells—the mind thinks and creates thoughts. Accept these thoughts with kindness, patience, and tolerance, allowing them to come and go. (Reader pause) Take a slow, deliberate breath.

- Next, place your awareness on the LEFT ANKLE.
- Move to the LEFT LOWER LEG—the SHIN and the CALF.
- Move to the where the SHIN and CALF connect to the KNEE.
- Move to the LEFT KNEECAP, the sides of the KNEE, the back of the KNEE.
- Move to where the KNEE connects to the THIGH.
- Pause. Now be aware of the entire LOWER LEFT LEG and KNEE, including their interior: the blood, bones, and muscles.

- Next, place your awareness on the LEFT THIGH, where it connects to the KNEE.
- Move to the MIDDLE THIGH. MOVE to the UPPER THIGH.
- Move to where the UPPER THIGH connects to the HIP.
- Place your awareness on the front, sides, and back of the ENTIRE LEFT THIGH.
- Pause. Now be aware of the entire LEFT THIGH,, including its interior: the blood, bones, and muscles.

Take a moment to notice any thoughts, emotions, or physical sensations. (Reader pause) Pay particular attention to any recurring thoughts or thought patterns you may be experiencing. Allow these thoughts to come and go, seeing them as a natural part of your mind. Just like the eyes see, the ears hear, and the nose smells—the mind thinks and creates thoughts. Accept these thoughts with kindness, patience, and tolerance, allowing them to come and go. (Reader pause) Take a slow, deliberate breath.

- Now place your awareness on the bottom of the RIGHT FOOT.
- Move to the HEEL, the ARCH, the BALL, and now the TOES.

- Move to the RIGHT BIG TOE—the tip, bottom, and top.
- Move to the 5th TOE, the 4th TOE, the 3rd TOE, and now the 2nd TOE.
- Be aware of the tips, bottoms, and tops of ALL the TOES.
- Place your awareness on the TOP of the FOOT.
- Move to the ACHILLES TENDON.
- Pause. Now be aware of the ENTIRE RIGHT FOOT, including its interior: the blood, bones, and muscles.

Take a moment to notice any thoughts, emotions, or physical sensations. (Reader pause) Pay particular attention to any recurring thoughts or thought patterns you may be experiencing. Allow these thoughts to come and go, seeing them as a natural part of your mind. Just like the eyes see, the ears hear, and the nose smells—the mind thinks and creates thoughts. Accept these thoughts with kindness, patience, and tolerance, allowing them to come and go. (Reader pause) Take a slow, deliberate breath.

- Next, place your awareness on the RIGHT ANKLE.
- Move to the RIGHT LOWER LEG—the SHIN and the CALF.
- Move to the where the SHIN and CALF connect to the KNEE.
- Move to the RIGHT KNEECAP, the sides of the KNEE, the back of the KNEE.
- Move to where the KNEE connects to the THIGH.
- Pause. Now be aware of the entire LOWER RIGHT LEG and KNEE, including their interior: the blood, bones, and muscles.
- Next, place your awareness on the RIGHT THIGH, where it connects to the knee.
- Move to the MIDDLE THIGH. MOVE to the UPPER THIGH. Move to where the UPPER THIGH connects to the HIP.

- Place your awareness on the front, sides, and back of the ENTIRE RIGHT THIGH.
- Pause. Now be aware of the entire RIGHT THIGH,, including its interior: the blood, bones, and muscles.

Take a moment to notice any thoughts, emotions, or physical sensations. (Reader pause) Pay particular attention to any recurring thoughts or thought patterns you may be experiencing. Allow these thoughts to come and go, seeing them as a natural part of your mind. Just like the eyes see, the ears hear, and the nose smells—the mind thinks and creates thoughts. Accept these thoughts with kindness, patience, and tolerance, allowing them to come and go. (Reader pause) Take a slow, deliberate breath.

The Region of Reproduction, Digestion, Assimilation, and Elimination: Pelvis, Abdomen and Lower Back

- Next, place your awareness on the PELVIS, the GENITALS, and the BOTTOM.
- Move to where the THIGHS, BOTTOM, TAILBONE, and GENITALS all meet.
- Next, place your awareness on the ABDOMEN, the BELLY, and the BELLY BUTTON.
- Now place your awareness on the LOWER BACK and LOWER SPINAL CORD.
- Pause. Be aware of the entire PELVIC, ABDOMEN, and LOWER BACK REGIONS including their interior: the blood, bones, muscles, and internal organs.

Take a moment to notice any thoughts, emotions, or physical sensations. (Reader pause) Pay particular attention to any recurring thoughts or thought patterns you may be experiencing. Allow these thoughts to come and go, seeing them as a natural part of your mind. Just like the eyes see, the ears hear, and the nose smells—the mind thinks and creates thoughts. Accept these thoughts with kindness, patience, and tolerance, allowing them to come and go. (Reader pause) Take a slow, deliberate breath.

The Region of Blood Circulation and Oxygenation: Chest, Heart and Back

- Next, place your awareness on the SOLAR PLEXUS, between the BELLY BUTTON and the HEART.
- Move to the RIBS and STERNUM, the LOWER, MID and UPPER CHEST, the HEART, the SIDES of the CHEST below the ARM PITS.
- Now place your awareness on the MID REGION of the BACK and now the UPPER BACK.
- Place your awareness on the lungs. Notice how the entire CHEST REGION inflates and deflates with each breath.
- Pause. Be aware of the entire CHEST, MID BACK and UPPER BACK REGIONS including their interior: the blood, bones, muscles, and internal organs.

Take a moment to notice any thoughts, emotions, or physical sensations. (Reader pause) Pay particular attention to any recurring thoughts or thought patterns you may be experiencing. Allow these thoughts to come and go, seeing them as a natural part of your mind. Just like the eyes see, the ears hear, and the nose smells—the mind thinks and creates thoughts. Accept these thoughts with kindness, patience, and tolerance, allowing them to come and go. (Reader pause) Take a slow, deliberate breath.

The Region of Physical Manipulation and Communicative Gesture: Fingers, Hands and Arms

- Next, place your awareness on the LEFT HAND.
- Place your awareness on the FINGERTIPS, the FINGERS, the JOINTS in the FINGERS.
- Move to where the FINGERS meet the PALM, the PALM, the BACK of the HAND, the WRIST.

158

- Move to the LOWER LEFT FOREARM, the upper LEFT FOREARM, and where they connect to the ELBOW.
- Move to the ELBOW, the UPPER LEFT ARM, the ARMPIT, the area where the UPPER LEFT ARM connects to the SHOULDER.
- Next, place your awareness on the RIGHT HAND.
- Place your awareness on the FINGERTIPS, the FINGERS, the JOINTS.
- Place your awareness where the FINGERS meet the PALM, the PALM, the BACK of the HAND, the WRIST.
- Move to the LOWER RIGHT FOREARM, the upper RIGHT FOREARM, and where they connect to the ELBOW.
- Move to the ELBOW, the UPPER RIGHT ARM, The ARM PIT, the area where the UPPER RIGHT ARM connects to the SHOULDER.
- Pause. Be aware of the entirety of both ARMS including the blood, bones, and muscles of each arm.

Take a moment to notice any thoughts, emotions, or physical sensations. (Reader pause) Pay particular attention to any recurring thoughts or thought patterns you may be experiencing. Allow these thoughts to come and go, seeing them as a natural part of your mind. Just like the eyes see, the ears hear, and the nose smells—the mind thinks and creates thoughts. Accept these thoughts with kindness, patience and tolerance, allowing them to come and go. (Reader pause) Take a slow, deliberate breath.

The Region of Communication, Thought, and Emotion: Shoulders, Face, and Head

- Next, place your awareness on the SHOULDERS, where the SHOULDER MUSCLES slope up to the NECK, the LOWER part of the NECK that connects to the CHEST, the ADAM'S APPLE, the SIDES of the

NECK, the BACK of the NECK that connects to the HEAD.

- Next, place your awareness on the JAW, the MOUTH, LIPS, CHEEKS, NOSE, EYES, EYELIDS, TEMPLES, FOREHEAD, EARS.
- Next, place your awareness on the interior cavities of this region.
- The INTERIOR OF THE MOUTH,—TEETH, GUMS, TONGUE, INNER THROAT, TONSILS;
- The NASAL INTERIOR—NOSTRILS and SINUS PASSAGES;
- The LEFT EAR—The LOBE, the EXTERIOR CANAL, the INNER EAR, the DEEP INNER EAR;
- The RIGHT EAR—The LOBE, the EXTERIOR CANAL, the INNER EAR, the DEEP INNER EAR.
- Next, place your awareness on the TOP of the HEAD, the SCALP, the SKULL, the HAIR, where the HEAD meets the TOP of the NECK.
- Next, place your awareness on the interior cavity of the HEAD and the BRAIN.
- Pause. Be aware of the entire SHOULDER, NECK, FACE, and HEAD REGION including their interiors: the blood, bones, muscles, and organs within.

Take a moment to notice any thoughts, emotions, or physical sensations. (Reader pause) Pay particular attention to any recurring thoughts or thought patterns you may be experiencing. Allow these thoughts to come and go, seeing them as a natural part of your mind. Just like the eyes see, the ears hear, and the nose smells—the mind thinks and creates thoughts. Accept these thoughts with kindness, patience, and tolerance, allowing them to come and go. (Reader pause) Take a slow, deliberate breath.

The Entire Body:
Briefly place your awareness on your entire body: Feet, Lower Legs, Knees, Thighs, Pelvis, Abdomen, Lower Back, Chest,

Upper Back, Fingers, Hands, Arms, Shoulders, Neck, Face, and Head.

End of The Thought Body Scan Exercise.
Know that this exercise has your best mindful intention to welcome and integrate all parts of your being—body, awareness, thought, and emotion. Slowly stand up. Move a little and stretch in a gentle way that feels good to you.

Notes:

Listen

Keep practicing this:

The Badass STOP Method:
- Stop
- Take 30 seconds to place your awareness on your entire body. Take a deep breath first: Feet, Lower legs, Knees, Thighs, Pelvis, Abdomen, Lower Back, Chest, Upper Back, Fingers, Hands, Arms, Shoulders, Neck, Face, and Head.
- Observe your emotions, thoughts, surroundings, and situation.
- Proceed.

Why do this?

Worth repeating: Because it feels great *and* it will dramatically improve the quality of your day.

Notes:

LESSON 21
EMOTION BODY SCAN

How to be mindful of emotions

You know those monster-sized cranes that are used to build skyscrapers? If you happen to be the guy or gal who operates those things—please don't earbud listen to this exercise while you're working. I really hate crooked skyscrapers.

The *Emotion Body Scan* can help you get in touch with difficult, daunting, and overwhelming emotions. The Emotion Body Scan can assist you in finding peace, equanimity, resiliency, and resolution relative to these emotions. With the Emotion Body Scan, we learn to embrace emotions (not run away or avoid them), locate them in the body, and accept them with kindness.

In doing this, what you will gain is referred to as *emotional intelligence*—an invaluable tool for responding to and accepting the full range of human emotion.

Same *To Do* list here, pal: one hour of uninterrupted time, a comfy place to lie down, and your favorite device to listen with. Ready, set, go…

The Emotion Body Scan Exercise:

Time required: 30-45 minutes

Preparation: Find a comfortable quiet space where you won't be disturbed. It's best to lie prone on your back in a relaxed, comfortable position as you listen or watch.

Task: Below is the script for reading and sharing *The General Body Scan Exercise.* I do *not* recommend a self-guided reading:

You can't read and tune into yourself at the same time. Listen to the audio or watch the video. You can also get together with a friend or relative and share it. If you are a teacher or guide, you can read the script to your class.

Three Deep Breaths: Begin by taking three deep breaths so that you learn with *both* body and mind.

1. Take a large inhale followed by a large exhale.
2. Take second large inhale followed by a large exhale.
3. Take third large inhale followed by a large exhale

Briefly tune into the current state of the body:
Pay attention to the general state of the body—tired, achy, hungry, relaxed, excited, hopeful, agitated, nervous, concerned, or perhaps not feeling much of anything. Allow everything to be as it is.

The Region of Mobility and Balance: Feet, Lower Legs, Knees and Thighs

- Begin by placing your awareness on the bottom of the LEFT FOOT.
- Move to the HEEL, the ARCH, the BALL, and now the TOES.
- Move to the LEFT BIG TOE—the tip, bottom, and top.
- Move to the 5th TOE, the 4th TOE, the 3rd TOE, and now the 2nd TOE.
- Be aware of tips, bottoms, and tops of ALL the TOES.
- Place your awareness on the TOP of the FOOT.
- Move to the ACHILLES TENDON.
- Pause. Now be aware of the ENTIRE LEFT FOOT, including its interior: the blood, bones, and muscles.

Take a moment to notice any thoughts, emotions, or physical sensations. Pay particular attention to any emotions that may arise. What is that emotion? Are you willing to take a closer look? Embrace the emotion. Turn toward it, not away from it.

166

Does that emotion have a particular feeling-place in your body? Where is that emotion in your body? Breath into that place on or in your body. Allow that emotion to be there. Accept it with kindness. Willingly, consciously, mindfully, simply allow that emotion to be there. Take a slow, deliberate breath.

- Next, place your awareness on the LEFT ANKLE.
- Move to the LEFT LOWER LEG—the SHIN and the CALF.
- Move to the where the SHIN and CALF connect to the KNEE.
- Move to the LEFT KNEECAP, the sides of the KNEE, the back of the KNEE.
- Move to where the KNEE connects to the THIGH.
- Pause. Now be aware of the entire LOWER LEFT LEG and KNEE, including their interior: the blood, bones, and muscle.

- Next, place your awareness on the LEFT THIGH, where it connects to the KNEE.
- Move to the MIDDLE THIGH. MOVE to the UPPER THIGH. Move to where the UPPER THIGH connects to the HIP.
- Place your awareness on the front, sides, and back of the ENTIRE LEFT THIGH.
- Pause. Now be aware of the entire LEFT THIGH including its interior: the blood, bones, and muscle.

Take a moment to notice any thoughts, emotions, or physical sensations. Pay particular attention to any emotions that may arise. What is that emotion? Are you willing to take a closer look? Embace the emotion. Turn toward it, not away from it. Does that emotion have a particular feeling-place in your body? Where is that emotion in your body? Breath into that place on or in your body. Allow that emotion to be there. Accept it with kindness. Willingly, consciously, mindfully, simply allow that emotion to be there. Take a slow, deliberate breath.

- Now place your awareness on the bottom of the RIGHT FOOT.
- Move to the HEEL, the ARCH, the BALL, and now the TOES.
- Move to the RIGHT BIG TOE—the tip, bottom, and top.
- Move to the 5th TOE, the 4th TOE, the 3rd TOE, and now the 2nd TOE.
- Be aware of the tips, bottoms, and tops of ALL the TOES.
- Place your awareness on the TOP of the FOOT.
- Move to the ACHILLES TENDON.
- Pause. Now be aware of the ENTIRE RIGHT FOOT, including its interior: the blood, bones, and muscles.

Take a moment to notice any thoughts, emotions, or physical sensations. Pay particular attention to any emotions that may arise. What is that emotion? Are you willing to take a closer look? Embace the emotion. Turn toward it, not away from it. Does that emotion have a particular feeling-place in your body? Where is that emotion in your body? Breath into that place on or in your body. Allow that emotion to be there. Accept it with kindness. Willingly, consciously, mindfully, simply allow that emotion to be there. Take a slow, deliberate breath.

- Next, place your awareness on the RIGHT ANKLE.
- Move to the RIGHT LOWER LEG—the SHIN and the CALF.
- Move to where the SHIN and CALF connect to the KNEE.
- Move to the RIGHT KNEECAP, the sides of the KNEE, the back of the KNEE.
- Move to where the KNEE connects to the THIGH.

- Pause. Now be aware of the entire LOWER RIGHT LEG and KNEE, including their interior: the blood, bones, and muscles.
- Next, place your awareness on the RIGHT THIGH, where it connects to the knee.
- Move to the MIDDLE THIGH. MOVE to the UPPER THIGH. Move to where the UPPER THIGH connects to the HIP.
- Place your awareness on the front, sides, and back of the ENTIRE RIGHT THIGH.
- Pause. Now be aware of the entire RIGHT THIGH, including its interior: the blood, bones, and muscle.

Take a moment to notice any thoughts, emotions, or physical sensations. Pay particular attention to any emotions that may arise. What is that emotion? Are you willing to take a closer look? Embace the emotion. Turn toward it not away from it. Does that emotion have a particular feeling-place in your body? Where is that emotion in your body? Breath into that place on or in your body. Allow that emotion to be there. Accept it with kindness. Willingly, consciously, mindfully simply allow that emotion to be there. Take a slow deliberate breath.

The Region of Reproduction, Digestion, Assimilation, and Elimination: Pelvis, Abdomen and Lower Back

- Next, place your awareness on the PELVIS, the GENITALS, and the BOTTOM.
- Move to where the THIGHS, BOTTOM, TAILBONE, and GENITALS all meet.
- Next, place your awareness on the ABDOMEN, the BELLY, and the BELLY BUTTON.
- Now place your awareness on the LOWER BACK and LOWER SPINAL CORD.
- Pause. Be aware of the entire PELVIC, ABDOMEN, and LOWER BACK REGIONS, including the interior: the blood, bones, muscles, and internal organs.

Take a moment to notice any thoughts, emotions, or physical sensations. Pay particular attention to any emotions that may arise. What is that emotion? Are you willing to take a closer look? Embace the emotion. Turn toward it, not away from it. Does that emotion have a particular feeling-place in your body? Where is that emotion in your body? Breath into that place on or in your body. Allow that emotion to be there. Accept it with kindness. Willingly, consciously, mindfully, simply allow that emotion to be there. Take a slow, deliberate breath.

The Region of Blood Circulation and Oxygenation: Chest, Heart and Back

- Next, place your awareness on the SOLAR PLEXUS, between the BELLY BUTTON and the HEART.
- Move to the RIBS and STERNUM, the LOWER, MID and UPPER CHEST, the HEART, the SIDES of the CHEST below the ARMPITS.
- Now place your awareness on the MID BACK and now the UPPER BACK.
- Place your awareness on the lungs. Notice how the entire CHEST REGION inflates and deflates with each breath.
- Pause. Be aware of the entire CHEST, MID BACK, and UPPER BACK REGIONS, including their interior: the blood, bones, muscles, and internal organs.

Take a moment to notice any thoughts, emotions, or physical sensations. Pay particular attention to any emotions that may arise. What is that emotion? Are you willing to take a closer look? Embace the emotion. Turn toward it, not away from it. Does that emotion have a particular feeling-place in your body? Where is that emotion in your body? Breath into that place on or in your body. Allow that emotion to be there. Accept it with kindness. Willingly, consciously, mindfully, simply allow that emotion to be there. Take a slow, deliberate breath.

The Region of Physical Manipulation and Communicative Gesture: Fingers, Hands and Arms

- Next, place your awareness on the LEFT HAND.
- Place your awareness on the FINGERTIPS, the FINGERS, the JOINTS in the FINGERS.
- Move to where the FINGERS meet the PALM, the PALM, the BACK of the HAND, the WRIST.
- Move to the LOWER LEFT FOREARM, the upper LEFT FOREARM, and where they connect to the ELBOW.
- Move to the the ELBOW, the UPPER LEFT ARM, the ARMPIT, the area where the UPPER LEFT ARM connects to the SHOULDER.
- Next, place your awareness on the RIGHT HAND.
- Place your awareness on the FINGERTIPS, the FINGERS, the JOINTS of the FINGERS.
- Move to where the fingers meet the PALM, the PALM, the BACK of the HAND, the WRIST.
- Move to the LOWER RIGHT FOREARM, the upper RIGHT FOREARM, and where they connect to the ELBOW.
- Move to the ELBOW, the UPPER RIGHT ARM, the ARMPIT, the area where the UPPER RIGHT ARM connects to the SHOULDER.
- Pause. Be aware of the entirety of both ARMS including their interior: the blood, bones, and muscles of each arm.

Take a moment to notice any thoughts, emotions, or physical sensations. Pay particular attention to any emotions that may arise. What is that emotion? Are you willing to take a closer look? Embace the emotion. Turn toward it, not away from it. Does that emotion have a particular feeling-place in your body? Where is that emotion in your body? Breath into that

171

place on or in your body. Allow that emotion to be there. Accept it with kindness. Willingly, consciously, mindfully, simply allow that emotion to be there. Take a slow deliberate breath.

The Region of Communication, Thought, and Emotion: Shoulders, Face, and Head

- Next, place your awareness on the SHOULDERS, where the SHOULDER MUSCLES slope up to the NECK, the LOWER part of the NECK that connects to the CHEST, the ADAM'S APPLE, the SIDES of the NECK, the BACK of the NECK that connects to the HEAD.
- Next, place your awareness on the JAW, the MOUTH, LIPS, CHEEKS, NOSE, EYES, EYELIDS, TEMPLES, FOREHEAD, EARS.
- Next, place your awareness on the INTERIOR OF THE MOUTH,, including TEETH, GUMS, TONGUE, INNER THROAT, TONSILS.
- Move to the NASAL INTERIOR, including NOSTRILS and SINUS PASSAGES.
- The LEFT EAR—the LOBE, the EXTERIOR CANAL, the INNER EAR, the DEEP INNER EAR;
- The RIGHT EAR—the LOBE, the EXTERIOR CANAL, the INNER EAR, the DEEP INNER EAR.
- Next, place your awareness on the TOP of the HEAD, the SCALP, the SKULL, the HAIR, where the HEAD meets the TOP of the NECK.
- Next, place your awareness on the interior cavity of the HEAD and the BRAIN.
- Pause. Be aware of the entire SHOULDER, NECK, FACE, and HEAD REGIONS including their interior: the blood, bones, muscles, and organs within.

Take a moment to notice any thoughts, emotions, or physical sensations. Pay particular attention to any emotions that may arise. What is that emotion? Are you willing to take a closer look? Embace the emotion. Turn toward it, not away from it. Does that emotion have a particular feeling-place in your body? Where is that emotion in your body? Breath into that place on or in your body. Allow that emotion to be there. Accept it with kindness. Willingly, consciously, mindfully, simply allow that emotion to be there. Take a slow, deliberate breath.

The Entire Body
Briefly place your awareness on your entire body: Feet, Lower Legs, Knees, Thighs, Pelvis, Abdomen, Lower Back, Chest, Upper Back, Fingers, Hands, Arms, Shoulders, Neck, Face, and Head.

End of The Emotion Body Scan Exercise
Know that this exercise has your best mindful intention to welcome and integrate all parts of your being—body, awareness, thought, and emotion. Slowly stand up. Move a little and stretch in a gentle way that feels good to you.

Lesson 21:
Emotion Body Scan

Listen

The Badass STOP Method:

- Stop.
- Take 30 seconds to place your awareness on your entire body: Take a deep breath first: Feet, Lower legs, Knees, Thighs, Pelvis, Abdomen, Lower Back, Chest, Upper Back, Fingers, Hands, Arms, Shoulders, Neck, Face and Head.
- Observe your emotions, thoughts, surroundings and situation.
- Proceed.

Why do this?

"When life gets you down, you know what you gotta do? Just keep swimming, just keep swimming."

–Dory / Finding Nemo

Just keep doing this.

Notes:

LESSON 22
PAIN BODY SCAN

How to be mindful of pain

This is the part where I invite you to go swimming in the ocean with me and you get stung by jellyfish. No jellyfish this time. I promise.

This exercise teaches you the possibility of experiencing pain directly without reaction or negative thoughts, which exacerbate the pain. In this exercise, mindful awareness explores the subtle nuances of body sensation, pain, thoughts, and feelings. Mindful awareness then notices the difference between actual pain and pain reaction. Out of this arises equanimity and compassion, which allow you to accept and understand the—painful—experience you are going through without judgment or analysis of it.

You got this: one hour of uninterrupted time, a comfy place to lie down, and your favorite device to listen with. Ready, set, go…

The Pain Body Scan Exercise:

Time required: 30-45 minutes

Preparation: Find a comfortable quiet space where you won't be disturbed. It's best to lie prone on your back in a relaxed, comfortable position as you listen or watch.

Task: Below is the script for reading and sharing *The General Body Scan Exercise.* I do *not* recommend a self-guided reading: You can't read and tune into yourself at the same time. Listen to the audio or watch the video. You can also get together with a friend or relative and share it.   If you are a teacher or guide, you can read the script to your class.

Three Deep Breaths: Begin by taking three deep breaths so that you learn with *both* body and mind.

1. Take a large inhale followed by a large exhale.
2. Take second large inhale followed by a large exhale.
3. Take third large inhale followed by a large exhale

Briefly tune into the current state of the body:
Pay attention to the general state of the body—tired, achy, hungry, relaxed, excited, hopeful, agitated, nervous, concerned, or perhaps not feeling much of anything. Allow everything to be as it is.

The Region of Mobility and Balance: Feet, Lower Legs, Knees and Thighs

- Begin by placing your awareness on the bottom of the LEFT FOOT.
- Move to the HEEL, the ARCH, the BALL, and now the TOES.
- Move to the LEFT BIG TOE—the tip, bottom, and top.
- Move to the 5th TOE, the 4th TOE, the 3rd TOE, and now the 2nd TOE.
- Be aware of tips, bottoms, and tops of ALL the TOES.
- Place your awareness on the TOP of the FOOT. Move to the ACHILLES TENDON.
- Pause. Now be aware of the ENTIRE LEFT FOOT, including its interior: the blood, bones, and muscles.

Take a moment to notice any thoughts, emotions, or physical sensations. Pay particular attention to any pain you may be experiencing. Drop whatever commentary or evaluation you may have about the pain experience in favor of seeing and sensing the pain experience directly in and of itself. Carefully explore the particular sensations that make it up—hardness or softness, warmth or coolness, tingling, tenseness, pressure, burning, throbbing, lightness, and so on. Let your awareness become as intimate with the pain experience as you can. Notice what happens to the sensations as you are mindful of them. Do they become stronger or weaker, larger or smaller, or do they stay the same? Take a slow, deliberate breath.

- Next, place your awareness on the LEFT ANKLE.
- Move to the LEFT LOWER LEG—the SHIN and the CALF.
- Move to the where the SHIN and CALF connect to the KNEE.
- Move to the LEFT KNEE CAP, the sides of the KNEE, the back of the KNEE.
- Move to where the KNEE connects to the THIGH.
- Pause. Now be aware of the entire LOWER LEFT LEG and KNEE, including their interior: the blood, bones, and muscle.

- Next, place your awareness on the LEFT THIGH, where it connects to the KNEE.
- Move to the MIDDLE THIGH. MOVE to the UPPER THIGH. Move to where the UPPER THIGH connects to the HIP.
- Place your awareness on the front, sides, and back of the ENTIRE LEFT THIGH.
- Pause. Now be aware of the entire LEFT THIGH, including its interior: the blood, bones, and muscle.

Take a moment to notice any thoughts, emotions, or physical sensations. Pay particular attention to any pain you may be experiencing. Drop whatever commentary or evaluation you may have about the pain experience in favor of seeing and sensing the pain experience directly in and of itself. Carefully explore the particular sensations that make it up—hardness or softness, warmth or coolness, tingling, tenseness, pressure, burning, throbbing, lightness, and so on. Let your awareness become as intimate with the pain experience as you can. Notice what happens to the sensations as you are mindful of them. Do they become stronger or weaker, larger or smaller, or do they stay the same? Take a slow, deliberate breath.

- Now place your awareness on the bottom of the RIGHT FOOT.
- Move to the HEEL, the ARCH, the BALL, and now the TOES.
- Move to the RIGHT BIG TOE—the tip, bottom, and top.
- Move to the 5th TOE, the 4th TOE, the 3rd TOE, and now the 2nd TOE.
- Be aware of the tips, bottoms, and tops of ALL the TOES.
- Place your awareness on the TOP of the FOOT. Move to the ACHILLES TENDON.
- Pause. Now be aware of the ENTIRE RIGHT FOOT, including its interior: the blood, bones, and muscles.

Take a moment to notice any thoughts, emotions, or physical sensations. Pay particular attention to any pain you may be experiencing. Drop whatever commentary or evaluation you may have about the pain experience in favor of seeing and sensing the pain experience directly in and of itself. Carefully explore the particular sensations that make it up—hardness or softness, warmth or coolness, tingling, tenseness, pressure, burning, throbbing, lightness, and so on. Let your awareness become as intimate with the pain experience as you can. Notice what happens to the sensations as you are mindful of them. Do they become stronger or weaker, larger or smaller, or do they stay the same? Take a slow, deliberate breath.

- Next, place your awareness on the RIGHT ANKLE.
- Move to the RIGHT LOWER LEG—the SHIN and the CALF.
- Move to where the SHIN and CALF connect to the KNEE.
- Move to the RIGHT KNEE CAP, the sides of the KNEE, the back of the KNEE.

- Move to where the KNEE connects to the THIGH.
- Pause. Now be aware of the entire LOWER RIGHT LEG and KNEE, including their interior: the blood, bones, and muscles.

- Next, place your awareness on the RIGHT THIGH, where it connects to the knee.
- Move to the MIDDLE THIGH. MOVE to the UPPER THIGH. Move to where the UPPER THIGH connects to the HIP.
- Place your awareness on the front, sides, and back of the ENTIRE RIGHT THIGH.
- Pause. Now be aware of the entire RIGHT THIGH, including its interior: the blood, bones, and muscles.

Take a moment to notice any thoughts, emotions, or physical sensations. Pay particular attention to any pain you may be experiencing. Drop whatever commentary or evaluation you may have about the pain experience in favor of seeing and sensing the pain experience directly in and of itself. Carefully explore the particular sensations that make up the pain— hardness or softness, warmth or coolness, tingling, tenseness, pressure, burning, throbbing, lightness, and so on. Let your awareness become as intimate with the pain experience as you can. Notice what happens to the sensations as you are mindful of them. Do they become stronger or weaker, larger or smaller, or do they stay the same? Take a slow, deliberate breath.

The Region of Reproduction, Digestion, Assimilation, and Elimination: Pelvis, Abdomen and Lower Back

- Next, place your awareness on the PELVIS, the GENITALS, and the BOTTOM.
- Move to where the THIGHS, BOTTOM, TAILBONE, and GENITALS all meet.
- Next, place your awareness on the ABDOMEN, the BELLY, and the BELLY BUTTON.

- Now place your awareness on the LOWER BACK and LOWER SPINAL CORD.
- Pause. Be aware of the entire PELVIC, ABDOMEN, and LOWER BACK REGION, including the interior: the blood, bones, muscles, and internal organs.

Take a moment to notice any thoughts, emotions, or physical sensations. Pay particular attention to any pain you may be experiencing. Drop whatever commentary or evaluation you may have about the pain experience in favor of seeing and sensing the pain experience directly in and of itself. Carefully explore the particular sensations that make up the pain— hardness or softness, warmth or coolness, tingling, tenseness, pressure, burning, throbbing, lightness, and so on. Let your awareness become as intimate with the pain experience as you can. Notice what happens to the sensations as you are mindful of them. Do they become stronger or weaker, larger or smaller, or do they stay the same? Take a slow, deliberate breath.

The Region of Blood Circulation and Oxygenation: Chest, Heart, and Back

- Next, place your awareness on the SOLAR PLEXUS between the BELLY BUTTON and the HEART.
- Move to the RIBS and STERNUM, the LOWER, MID and UPPER CHEST, the HEART, the SIDES of the CHEST, below the ARMPITS.
- Now place your awareness on the MID REGION of the BACK and now the UPPER BACK.
- Place your awareness on the lungs. Notice how the entire CHEST REGION inflates and deflates with each breath.
- Pause. Be aware of the entire CHEST, MID BACK, and UPPER BACK REGION including the interior: the blood, bones, muscles, and internal organs.

Take a moment to notice any thoughts, emotions, or physical sensations. Pay particular attention to any pain you may be

182

experiencing. Drop whatever commentary or evaluation you may have about the pain experience in favor of seeing and sensing the pain experience directly in and of itself. Carefully explore the particular sensations that make up the pain— hardness or softness, warmth or coolness, tingling, tenseness, pressure, burning, throbbing, lightness, and so on. Let your awareness become as intimate with the pain experience as you can. Notice what happens to the sensations as you are mindful of them. Do they become stronger or weaker, larger or smaller, or do they stay the same? Take a slow, deliberate breath.

The Region of Physical Manipulation and Communicative Gesture: Fingers, Hands, and Arms

- Next, place your awareness on the LEFT HAND.
- Place your awareness on the FINGERTIPS, the FINGERS, the JOINTS in the FINGERS.
- Move to where the FINGERS meet the PALM, the PALM, the BACK of the HAND, the WRIST.
- Move to the LOWER LEFT FOREARM and the UPPER LEFT FOREARM, where they connect to the ELBOW.
- Move to the ELBOW, the UPPER LEFT ARM, the ARMPIT, the area where the UPPER LEFT ARM connects to the SHOULDER.
- Next, place your awareness on the RIGHT HAND.
- Place your awareness on the FINGERTIPS, the FINGERS, the JOINTS in the FINGERS.
- Move to where the fingers meet the PALM, the PALM, the BACK of the HAND, the WRIST.
- Move to the LOWER RIGHT FOREARM and the UPPER RIGHT FOREARM, where they connect to the ELBOW.
- Move to the ELBOW, the UPPER RIGHT ARM, the ARMPIT, the area where the UPPER RIGHT ARM connects to the SHOULDER.

- Pause. Be aware of the entirety of both ARMS including their interior: the blood, bones, and muscles of each arm.

Take a moment to notice any thoughts, emotions, or physical sensations. Pay particular attention to any pain you may be experiencing. Drop whatever commentary or evaluation you may have about the pain experience in favor of seeing and sensing the pain experience directly in and of itself. Carefully explore the particular sensations that make up the pain— hardness or softness, warmth or coolness, tingling, tenseness, pressure, burning, throbbing, lightness, and so on. Let your awareness become as intimate with the pain experience as you can. Notice what happens to the sensations as you are mindful of them. Do they become stronger or weaker, larger or smaller, or do they stay the same? Take a slow, deliberate breath.

The Region of Communication, Thought, and Emotion: Shoulders, Face, and Head

- Next, place your awareness on the SHOULDERS, where the SHOULDER MUSCLES slope up to the NECK, The LOWER part of the NECK that connects to the CHEST, the ADAM'S APPLE, the SIDES of the NECK, the BACK of the NECK that connects to the HEAD.
- Next, place your awareness on the JAW, the MOUTH, LIPS, CHEEKS, NOSE, EYES, EYELIDS, TEMPLES, FOREHEAD, EARS.
- Next, place your awareness on the INTERIOR of the MOUTH, including TEETH, GUMS, TONGUE, INNER THROAT, TONSILS.
- Move to the NASAL INTERIOR, including NOSTRILS and SINUS PASSAGES.
- Move to the LEFT EAR—the LOBE, the EXTERIOR CANAL, the INNER EAR, the DEEP INNER EAR.
- Move to the RIGHT EAR—the LOBE, the EXTERIOR CANAL, the INNER EAR, the DEEP INNER EAR.

- Next, place your awareness on the TOP of the HEAD, the SCALP, the SKULL, the HAIR, where the HEAD meets the TOP of the NECK.
- Next, place your awareness on the interior cavity of the HEAD and the BRAIN.
- Pause. Be aware of the entire SHOULDER, NECK, FACE and HEAD REGION, including the interior: the blood, bones, muscles, and organs within.

Take a moment to notice any thoughts, emotions, or physical sensations. Pay particular attention to any pain you may be experiencing. Drop whatever commentary or evaluation you may have about the pain experience in favor of seeing and sensing the pain experience directly in and of itself. Carefully explore the particular sensations that make up the pain—hardness or softness, warmth or coolness, tingling, tenseness, pressure, burning, throbbing, lightness, and so on. Let your awareness become as intimate with the pain experience as you can. Notice what happens to the sensations as you are mindful of them. Do they become stronger or weaker, larger or smaller, or do they stay the same? Take a slow, deliberate breath.

The Entire Body:
Briefly place your awareness on your entire body: Feet, Lower Legs, Knees, Thighs, Pelvis, Abdomen, Lower Back, Chest, Upper Back, Fingers, Hands, Arms, Shoulders, Neck, Face, and Head.

End of The Pain Body Scan Exercise
Know that this exercise has your best mindful intention to welcome and integrate all parts of your being—body, awareness, thought, and emotion. Slowly stand up. Move a little and stretch in a gentle way that feels good to you.

Practice this anytime and anyplace:

The Badass STOP Method:
- Stop.
- Take 30 seconds to place your awareness on your entire body. Take a deep breath first: Feet, Lower legs, Knees, Thighs, Pelvis, Abdomen, Lower Back, Chest, Upper Back, Fingers, Hands, Arms, Shoulders, Neck, Face, and Head.
- Observe your emotions, thoughts, surroundings, and situation.
- Proceed.

Why do this?

Lenny knows.

Notes:

LESSON 23
MINDFUL SMART PHONE

How to butt-dial mindfully

Now that you've got a few mindfulness exercises under your belt, let's put your new skills to use during hum-drum, everyday activities. Let's get mindfully jiggety while talking with someone in person, on the phone, and on a computer.

The Mindful Communication Exercise:

Time required: 30-45 minutes

Preparation: Find a comfortable quiet space where you won't be disturbed. It's best to remain seated in a relaxed, comfortable position for this one.

Task: Below is the script for reading and sharing *The Mindful Communication Exercise.* You can read this to yourself, listen to the audio, or get together with a friend or relative and share it. If you're a teacher or guide, you can read the script to your class.

Three Deep Breaths: Begin by taking three deep breaths so that you learn with *both* body and mind.

1. Take a large inhale followed by a large exhale.
2. Take second large inhale followed by a large exhale.
3. Take third large inhale followed by a large exhale.

Briefly tune into the current state of the body:
Pay attention to the general state of the body—tired, achy, hungry, relaxed, excited, hopeful, agitated, nervous, concerned, or perhaps not feeling much of anything. Allow everything to

189

be as it is.

Super Brief Body Scan:
Take 30 seconds to place your awareness on your entire body: Feet, Lower Legs, Knees, Thighs, Pelvis, Abdomen, Lower Back, Chest, Upper Back, Fingers, Hands, Arms, Shoulders, Neck, Face, and Head.

Visualize yourself—from your point of view—talking in person with a friend, relative, coworker, or stranger.

- Picture this person seated or standing in front of you.
- See, hear, and feel this conversation.
- Notice when this friend, relative, coworker, or stranger talks.
- Notice when you talk.
- Take a deep breath.
- Notice your whole body from head to toe.
- Now, notice empty, silent, mindful awareness. …that is doing the noticing.
- Again—see and hear yourself talking.
- Notice the act of talking.
- Notice that you are mindfully aware of the act of talking.

Notice that this mindful awareness is always present under all conditions. The next time you find yourself talking with a friend, relative, coworker, or stranger—you have permission to be mindfully aware of it.

Take a deep breath.

Visualize yourself—from your point of view—talking with someone on your phone.

- Picture yourself holding the phone up to your ear and mouth.
- See, hear, and feel the conversation.

- Notice when the person on the other end talks.
- Notice when you talk.
- Take a deep breath.
- Notice your whole body from head to toe.
- Now, notice empty, silent, mindful awareness ...that is doing the noticing.
- Again—see and hear yourself talking on the phone.
- Notice the act of talking on the phone.
- Notice that you are mindfully aware of the act of talking on the phone.

Notice that this mindful awareness is always present under all conditions. The next time you find yourself talking on the phone, you have permission to be mindfully aware of it.

Take a deep breath.

Visualize yourself—from your point of view—emailing or texting on a computer or device.

- Picture yourself seated in front of your computer or device.
- See yourself writing the email or text.
- See yourself receiving a reply.
- Take a deep breath.
- Notice your whole body from head to toe.
- And now, notice empty, silent, mindful awareness...that is doing the noticing.
- Again—see yourself emailing or texting on a computer or device.
- Notice the act of emailing or texting.
- Notice that you are mindfully aware of the act of emailing or texting.

Notice that this mindful awareness is always present under all conditions. The next time you find yourself emailing or texting, you have permission to be mindfully aware of it.

Lesson 23:
Mindful Smart Phone

Listen

Spiritual Badass Homework:

Yep. You guessed it.

The Badass STOP Method:

- Stop.
- Take 30 seconds to place your awareness on your entire body. Take a deep breath first: Feet, Lower legs, Knees, Thighs, Pelvis, Abdomen, Lower Back, Chest, Upper Back, Fingers, Hands, Arms, Shoulders, Neck, Face, and Head.
- Observe your emotions, thoughts, surroundings and situation.
- Proceed.

Why do this?

Hint: This is not just an exercise. It's a way of living, being breathing, resting, moving, and relating to life.

Notes:

LESSON 24
MINDFUL MOUTH

How to eat, drink, snack, and yes—even smoke—mindfully

I'm no saint and I'm definitely not here to judge. This spiritual badass likes spaghetti, salad, chocolate chip cookies, tequila, and cigars—and sometimes all in one evening; but I also have a healthy distance from these bad habits. I can stop eating sugar, drinking alcohol, or smoking cigars at the drop of a hat. As an example, during the holidays in November and December, I like to detox and abstain from alcohol.

I'm sharing all this with you because I want you to know that you can be a spiritual badass and still do some pretty stupid things—including drinking cheap beer and smoking cigarettes. BUT *if you're gonna do that shit*, at least do it *mindfully* so that you control them and not the other way around.

Being mindful—of what you put in your mouth; of what you're eating; of what you're drinking; of what you're smoking—goes a long way in preventing *mindless,* damaging addiction.

If you struggle with knee-jerk reactive smoking, drinking, and eating—this exercise will help you gain some space. *It will help you say no, should you want to.*

The Mindful Mouth Exercise:

Time required: 30-45 minutes

Preparation: Find a comfortable quiet space where you won't be disturbed. It's best to remain seated in a relaxed, comfortable position for this one.

195

Task: Below is the script for reading and sharing *The Mindful Mouth Exercise.* You can read this to yourself, listen to the audio, or get together with a friend or relative and share it. If you're a teacher or guide, you can read the script to your class.

Three Deep Breaths: Begin by taking three deep breaths so that you learn with *both* body and mind.

1. Take a large inhale followed by a large exhale.
2. Take second large inhale followed by a large exhale.
3. Take third large inhale followed by a large exhale.

Briefly tune into the current state of the body:
Pay attention to the general state of the body—tired, achy, hungry, relaxed, excited, hopeful, agitated, nervous, concerned, or perhaps not feeling much of anything. Allow everything to be as it is.

Super Brief Body Scan:
Take a minute to place your awareness on your entire body: Feet, Lower Legs, Knees, Thighs, Pelvis, Abdomen, Lower Back, Chest, Upper Back, Fingers, Hands, Arms, Shoulders, Neck, Face, and Head.

Visualize yourself—from your point of view—eating a healthy lunch.

- Picture yourself seated at a table with a healthy lunch on a plate.
- Slowly begin to eat the lunch.
- Notice the smelling, chewing, swallowing.
- Notice the pleasure of eating.
- Take a deep breath.
- Notice your whole body from head to toe.
- And now, notice empty, silent, mindful awareness. …that is doing the noticing.
- Again—picture yourself eating a healthy lunch.
- Notice the act of eating.

196

- Notice that you are mindfully aware of the act of eating.

Notice that this mindful awareness is always present under all conditions. The next time you find yourself eating, you have permission to be mindfully aware of it.

Take a deep breath.

Visualize yourself—from your point of view—drinking a can of soda.

- Picture yourself seated in a lounge chair drinking a can of soda.
- Slowly begin to drink the soda.
- Notice the smelling, tasting, swallowing.
- Notice the pleasure of drinking.
- Take a deep breath.
- Notice your whole body from head to toe.
- And now, notice empty, silent, mindful awareness …that is doing the noticing.
- Again—picture yourself drinking a can of soda.
- Notice the act of drinking.
- Notice that you are mindfully aware of the act of drinking.

Notice that this mindful awareness is always present under all conditions. The next time you find yourself drinking, you have permission to be mindfully aware of it.

Take a deep breath.

Visualize yourself—from your point of view—snacking on a bag of Doritos.

- Picture yourself seated at your desk snacking on a bag of Doritos.
- Slowly begin to eat the Doritos.

- Notice the smelling, chewing, swallowing.
- Notice the pleasure of eating.
- Take a deep breath.
- Notice your whole body from head to toe.
- And now, notice empty, silent, mindful awareness…that is doing the noticing.
- Again—picture yourself eating a bag of Doritos.
- Notice the act of eating.
- Notice that you are mindfully aware of the act of eating.

Notice that this mindful awareness is always present under all conditions. The next time you find yourself eating a bag of Doritos (or any other snack), you have permission to be mindfully aware of it.

Take a deep breath.

Visualize yourself—from your point of view—smoking a cigarette.

- Picture yourself standing outside, smoking a cigarette.
- Slowly begin to smoke.
- Notice the drawing, inhaling, and exhaling.
- Notice the pleasure of smoking.
- Take a deep breath.
- Notice your whole body from head to toe.
- And now, notice empty, silent, mindful awareness…that is doing the noticing.
- Again—picture yourself smoking a cigarette.
- Notice the act of smoking.
- Notice that you are mindfully aware of the act of smoking.

Notice that this mindful awareness is always present under all conditions. The next time you find yourself smoking, you have permission to be mindfully aware of it.

The next time you eat, drink, or smoke something, before you do so, practice the exercise below so you can be mindful before you do it and have the option to say no.

The Badass STOP Method:

- Stop.
- Take 30 seconds to place your awareness on your entire body. Take a deep breath first: Feet, Lower Legs, Knees, Thighs, Pelvis, Abdomen, Lower Back, Chest, Upper Back, Fingers, Hands, Arms, Shoulders, Neck, Face, and Head.
- Observe your emotions, thoughts, surroundings and situation.
- Proceed.

Why do this?

This will help you with bad habits. Again—this is not just an exercise. It's a way of living, being, breathing, resting, moving, and relating to life.

LESSON 25
MINDFUL ACTIVITY

How to drive, shop, clean and walk in the park mindfully

Early on during my spiritual badass adventure, I found myself at the grocery store in the midst of a full-on, superhero-like, blissed out, mindful, orgasmic at-one-with-the universe state. It was fucking awesome. But ever since that time, this experience has completely fucked up my grocery shopping—*in a good way*! Often, when I go to the grocery, I find myself in a happy-as-shit, mindful space. It turns what is usually boring drudgery into a trip to Disney Land. I'm inviting you to experience the same...

This next exercise may not get your cosmic consciousness on (or who the hell knows? Maybe it will.), but it'll definitely make driving, shopping, cleaning, or walking in the park a tad bit better. That's good stuff in my opinion.

The Mindful Activity Exercise:

Time required: 30-45 minutes

Preparation: Find a comfortable quiet space where you won't be disturbed. It's best to remain seated in a relaxed, comfortable position for this one.

Task: Below is the script for reading and sharing *The Mindful Mouth Exercise.* You can read this to yourself, listen to the audio, or get together with a friend or relative and share it. If you're a teacher or guide, you can read the script to your class.

Three Deep Breaths: Begin by taking three deep breaths so that you learn with *both* body and mind.

1. Take a large inhale followed by a large exhale.
2. Take second large inhale followed by a large exhale.
3. Take third large inhale followed by a large exhale.

Briefly tune into the current state of the body:
Pay attention to the general state of the body—tired, achy, hungry, relaxed, excited, hopeful, agitated, nervous, concerned, or perhaps not feeling much of anything. Allow everything to be as it is.

Super Brief Body Scan:
Take a minute to place your awareness on your entire body: Feet, Lower Legs, Knees, Thighs, Pelvis, Abdomen, Lower Back, Chest, Upper Back, Fingers, Hands, Arms, Shoulders, Neck, Face, and Head.

Visualize yourself—from your point of view—driving your car.

- Picture yourself seated behind the wheel of your car.
- Slowly begin to drive the car.
- Notice the movement: the sight, sound, and feel of driving.
- Notice the concentration required to drive.
- Take a deep breath.
- Notice your whole body from head to toe.
- And now, notice empty, silent, mindful awareness ...that is doing the noticing.
- Again—picture yourself driving your car.
- Notice the act of driving.
- Notice that you are mindfully aware of the act of driving.

Notice that this mindful awareness is always present under all conditions. The next time you find yourself driving, you have permission to be mindfully aware of it.

Take a deep breath.

Visualize yourself—from your point of view—shopping at the grocery.

- Picture yourself shopping at your local grocery store.
- Slowly begin to shop down the aisles of your grocery store.
- Notice the movement: the sight, sound, and feeling of shopping.
- Notice the concentration required to shop.
- Take a deep breath.
- Notice your whole body from head to toe.
- And now notice empty, silent, mindful awareness ...that is doing the noticing.
- Again—picture yourself shopping at the grocery.
- Notice the act of shopping.
- Notice that you are mindfully aware of the act of shopping.

Notice that this mindful awareness is always present under all conditions. The next time you find yourself shopping, you have permission to be mindfully aware of it.

Take a deep breath.

Visualize yourself—from your point of view—cleaning your house

- Picture yourself cleaning your house.
- Slowly begin to sweep, mop, and scrub your house.
- Notice the movement: the sight, sound, and feeling of cleaning.
- Notice the concentration required to clean.
- Take a deep breath.

- Notice your whole body from head to toe.
- And now notice empty, silent, mindful awareness…that is doing the noticing.
- Again—picture yourself cleaning your house.
- Notice the act of cleaning.
- Notice that you are mindfully aware of the act of cleaning.

Notice that this mindful awareness is always present under all conditions. The next time you find yourself cleaning, you have permission to be mindfully aware of it.

Take a deep breath.

Visualize yourself—from your point of view—walking in the park.

- Picture yourself walking in the park.
- Slowly begin walk through the park.
- Notice the movement: the sight, sound, and feeling of walking.
- Notice the concentration required to walk.
- Take a deep breath.
- Notice your whole body from head to toe.
- And now notice empty, silent, mindful awareness…that is doing the noticing.
- Again—picture yourself walking in the park.
- Notice the act of walking.
- Notice that you are mindfully aware of the act of walking.

Notice that this mindful awareness is always present under all conditions. The next time you find yourself walking, you have permission to be mindfully aware of it.

Lesson 25:
Mindful Activity

Listen

I know this homework is repetitive, but it works. The point here is to be automatically mindful: breathing, noticing, being—without prompts, reminders, exercises, or tools. Do this shit enough and that's what'll happen. Now, go practice this next time you're doing the dishes, and see what happens...

The Badass STOP Method:
- Stop.
- Take 30 seconds to place your awareness on your entire body: Take a deep breath first. Feet, Lower Legs, Knees, Thighs, Pelvis, Abdomen, Lower Back, Chest, Upper Back, Fingers, Hands, Arms, Shoulders, Neck, Face, and Head.
- Observe your emotions, thoughts, surroundings and situation.
- Proceed.

Why do this?

Mindfully Live. Be. Breathe. Rest. Move. Walk. Run. Fly. Talk. Eat. Shit. Piss. Drink. Fuck. Dance. Cry. Shout. Laugh. Love. Hate. And watch your life completely change.

MINDFULNESS LETTER

Handwrite Me a Letter

Handwrite me a letter about your experience with *Spirituality for Badasses The Workbook Part Three: Mindfulness Lessons. Your letter will be 100% private and not shared.* I've provided a list of questions below you can use as a guide, or write whatever moves you.

Why do this?

Writing out your deepest thoughts, fears, confessions, and internal dialogues will be very helpful for your spiritual badass journey. *It will get you there quicker.* Writing, sharing, or confessing *to someone* gets it out of *you* and into the light of day, where it can heal, transform, and benefit. Also—writing by hand is better. We tend to be more honest with a pen in hand.

Mindfulness Letter Questions:

- Is it working? Can you report any ongoing effects of practicing mindfulness?
- Is your sense of mindfulness more defined?
- What's the hardest thing for you to be mindful of?
- What was the hardest mindfulness awareness exercise for you?
- Have there been any mindfulness breakthroughs or benefits you can point to?
- What area of your life do you think still needs more mindful attention and awareness?
- How's life?

Send it here:

PIE Publishing c/o J. Stewart Dixon
P.O. Box 32
Earlysville VA 22936

Notes:

Notes:

END PART 3

After you've completed *The Workbook* continue
your adventure with author J. Stewart Dixon.
Get Access to:
New Book Sneak Previews,
Online Courses, Videos, Humor,
Spiritual Badass Wisdom &
Swear Words for all.

Go here:
www.spiritualityforbadasses.com

PART 4

Ego Lessons

LESSON 26
EGO SOBERING TRUTH

How to recognize the constant activity of ego

Welcome to Part Four of *The Workbook: Ego Lessons.* Congratulations! You have just entered the big-boss-battle arena of ego. Your hero moment has finally arrived. There will be dragons. There will be earthquakes. There will be volcanoes. But you're a badass. You got this.

In this part, you're going to learn how to recognize ego. You'll learn how to see it, accept it, do battle with it, and dismantle it. Then, you'll learn to how to reconstitute it in a newer, healthier, and saner place: behind—*and secondary to*—awareness.

Here's a refresher regarding ego:

"Let's start with a simple definition of ego that adequately served me while on the spiritual path. Ego is my sense of identity: J. Stewart. Me. I. J.'s habits, desires, personality characteristics, limitations, weaknesses, insecurities, strengths, dreams, powers, skills, talents, the things he thinks about himself, and the things he thinks others think about him.

Ego as a whole is the J. *Identity Project.*

Like all human beings, the J. Identity Project is ultimately seeking love, security, comfort, peace, or happiness. The J. Identity Project is seeking pleasure and avoiding pain. This project is not so much a thing as it is an *activity.*

Therefore...

Ego is the activity of doing, working, socializing, performing, talking, thinking, dreaming, desiring, and longing...all in the name of seeking pleasure and avoiding pain. Seeking. Searching. Desiring. This is the constant never-ending activity of ego.

You do it, consciously or unconsciously. You do it aware of or ignorant of—*all the time*. Ego is wrapped up in every single facet of your existence.

Ego is an *activity*.

Once you finally begin to understand *and see* this constant activity, one very salient thing about it becomes apparent: ego never fulfills its promise.

No matter how plain, complex, ignorant, intelligent, fabulous, terrible, famous, unknown, stupendous, humble, weak, spiritual, creative, powerful—or badass—your grand ego-identity project grows to be, it never... truly... ultimately... *delivers*. It only leaves you wanting more. You never arrive at the ultimate life of fulfillment; the ego is constantly promising.

Ego is an *activity*.

Ego is an always-dangling carrot held on a string three feet in front of you. Try as you might, you never reach the carrot. *And*—you can't stop reaching.

Pretty gloomy, right? Actually—no. Not gloomy.

If this absolute bare-bones realization of ego's dead-end, nihilistic, sadistic promise was all there was to realize—then yes, this would be some pretty fucking gloomy shit indeed.

But the good news is this: There's something else to realize. And that *something* is the very thing that *sees ego* to begin with:

Awareness. Awareness sees ego.

Awareness *precedes* ego.

214

This is the beautiful and magical part of the whole badass spiritual process: at the same time you see and dismantle ego, you see and empower awareness...until their roles are reversed.

Awareness no longer takes a back seat. Awareness takes the pilot's seat and ego takes the back...co-pilot's seat.

This reversal of roles introduces a revolution in your life and, in many ways, becomes the defining feature of being a spiritual badass.

A few final thoughts, and then we'll move on to the exercise. In seeing ego, we are not bashing ego. There is no judgment going on here; I have no problem with ego. You need ego to function in this world. As a matter of fact, in a paradoxical way, ego needs to be your best friend—because you need its badass strength: To transcend or completely see the ego, you must have a big enough ego to think that you can actually transcend it. Go figure.

So again, ego is not the enemy. Your identity project is not bad. It is simply limited in its ability to deliver. Thus, it is of vital importance that you see ego and all its limitations.

Ego is an *activity.*"

Ego gets an F.

Let's look at another definition of ego. In Webster's Dictionary, ego is defined as "the self as distinguished from others." For our purposes, let us define "others" as this: *everything.*

The dictionary definition points to the fact that the "you" that you think you are is separate from, derivative of, and defined by some "other" outside of yourself. Examine "other" thoroughly and you will discover that it has unimaginable depth and scope: things, people, places, activities, thoughts, emotions, and dreams—from the most materialistic, dense and crass to the most ethereal, light and benign. "Other" is everything.

But who gives a shit about a dictionary definition, right? Because, ultimately—ego gets an F. It's got the whole fucking universe at its disposal to please you with—and it never, ever, ultimately delivers. Ego just wants more and more and more...

The lesson here is that you don't need to understand ego on a psychological level. You don't need to grasp all the philosophical implications of ego. All you have to do is see, understand, and *feel* how ego has failed you.

Okay, so no big deal: Ego gets an F. Ego has not been doing such a great job. So be it. Let's let off the pressure. Let's give ego a break. It has, to date, served you well and you can now thank it and love it and have compassion for it. Beautiful—it's imperfect. What a relief! What a relief to discover that ego and all its activities are imperfect. Now at least our expectations can be adjusted, and we can move on...

It's now time to enter the arena.

Some things you'll need during Part Four:

- A quiet place to sit or lie down
- Some uninterrupted free time
- Some badass courage
- A box of tissues
- A device to listen to (or watch) some exercises on.

Spiritual Badass Homework:

Grab your journal and scribble out a few answers:

- Does the idea of letting go of ego scare you?
- Are you dreading what's to come in this part?
- Where do you feel resistance, fear, or knots in your body regarding ego?
- What are you holding on to the most?
- What don't you want to let go of or give up?
- Do you trust or know that something saner, happier, and wiser will be there to replace ego?

Why do this?

It's a very good idea to begin practicing some cathartic writing around the process of dismantling ego. Letting go of ego is difficult and challenging. Releasing and facing your fears, heartbreak, pain, depression, and anxieties—on paper—will ultimately help you to do the same *internally*.

Notes:

Notes:

LESSON 27
FREE FALL

How to let go of everything

Dismantling ego can only be truly accomplished when there is equal understanding of *that* which sees, understands, accepts, and embraces the dismantling process. Falling *out* of ego reveals *that* which you are falling *into*: your truest spiritual badass self.

You've already read about and experienced this exercise with J. and Tenzin at "the drop" zipline and quarry at *Seven Dragons Sanctuary*. Let's revisit the exercise, with an emphasis on letting everything you hold dear about yourself and life...your entire ego-personality-project...go. Let's fall into the heart of who you really are.

The Freefall Exercise:

Time required: 30-45 minutes

Preparation: Find a comfortable quiet space where you won't be disturbed. It's best to remain seated for this one—in a relaxed, comfortable position.

Task: Below is the script for reading and sharing *The Freefall Exercise*. Read it here first to familiarize yourself with it. Then listen to the audio or get together with a friend or relative and share it. If you're a teacher or guide, you can read the script to your class.

Three Deep Breaths: Begin by taking three deep breaths so that you learn with *both* body and mind.

1. Take a large inhale followed by a large exhale.

2. Take a second large inhale followed by a large exhale.

3. Take a third large inhale followed by a large exhale.

Briefly tune into the current state of the body:
Pay attention to the general state of the body—tired, achy, hungry, relaxed, excited, hopeful, agitated, nervous, concerned, or perhaps not feeling much of anything. Allow everything to be as it is.

Brief Body Scan:
Take a few minutes to place your awareness on your entire body: Feet, Lower Legs, Knees, Thighs, Pelvis, Abdomen, Lower Back, Chest, Upper Back, Fingers, Hands, Arms, Shoulders, Neck, Face, and Head.

In this visualization, we begin by holding hands. I'll hold your hand for a little while and then, as you get comfortable, I'll let go and you'll be on your own.

Together, hand in hand, we walk through a rough, boulder-strewn desert environment. Permutations of natural brown, orange, red, and green colors splash over the landscape. We follow a single-track light brown dirt path through some scrub, rocks, and dry vegetation. The path winds around and down for a little while. Eventually, we arrive at a vast overlook and cliff edge.

Together we stand hand in hand at the edge of a tremendously deep ravine. The ravine is so deep, it's impossible to see bottom. As we peer over the edge, we see the light diminish into pure blackness. We are at the edge of the unknown itself. We are at the edge of complete mystery. We are at the edge of one way of life and the beginning of another.

Together we are going to jump off this cliff edge. We shuffle our feet closer and closer to the rim. Small pebbles crunch, give way, and spill over and down. Close your eyes. Take a deep breath. On the count of three—we are going to jump.

One.....Two....Three...

Together we jump. Our stomachs flutter deeply and hearts jump to our throats as a sensation of complete freefall overtakes us.

The air rushes by. We can see the side of the cliff zooming past us in a great blurry whirl of form and color. The sound of the air rushing through our limbs and bodies and ears is constant. We settle into this freefalling state. We surrender all control and effort. We are helpless in this state of complete freefall.

Slowly you relax and allow the falling to completely take you...deeper and deeper you relax... to the point where you are now enjoying the complete freedom, peace, and effortlessness of the fall. There is complete acceptance of the falling. Deep acceptance, gratitude, and freedom. You have absolutely no control. Just falling, falling, falling.

I am now going to let go of your hand and let you freefall on your own. We'll meet a little later at the top of the cliff...I let go of your hand, and you continue to fall on your own. The air rushes by; the cliff walls rush by.

You now begin the descent into darkness. The light is now quickly coming to an end. Farther and farther you fall. It gets darker and darker. And now, you are falling in pitch black darkness. You see nothing. You have no control, no guide, no escape. You are completely alone in the freefall. You fully accept your condition and circumstance.

You now fall into the absolute heart of awareness itself. You are completely aware of all experiences, bodily sensations, emotions, and thoughts...high or low, good or bad. You are unconditionally and absolutely aware. Aware—without hesitation, reluctance, fear, or reservation.

Take a deep breath.

You can now let go of the old you: your work, education, and hobbies…and see what is left.

Who you truly are is deeper, more permanent, and bigger than any of these things. Who you truly are is not defined or dependent upon work status, education level, or life interests. Notice who you truly are before these things.

Continue falling.

You can now let go of the old you: your family, friends, and relatives…and see what is left.

Who you truly are is deeper, more permanent, and bigger than any of these things. Who you truly are is not defined or dependent upon by family, friends, and relatives to be happy, content, confident, and at peace. Notice who you truly are before these things.

Continue falling.

You can now let go of the old you: your nationality, religion and heritage …and see what is left.

Who you truly are is deeper, bigger, and more badass than any of these things. Who you truly are doesn't depend upon nationality, religious belief, or ancestry to be happy, content, confident, and at peace. Notice who you truly are before these things.

Continue falling.

You can now let go of the old you: your gender, body type, and skin color…and see what is left.

Who you truly are is deeper, bigger, and more badass than any of these things. Who you truly are doesn't depend upon being male or female or being thin, heavy, tall, or short or having brown, black, or yellow skin to be happy, content, confident, and at peace. Notice who you truly are before these things.

Continue falling.

You can now let go of the old you: your birth date, birthplace, and name...and see what is left.

Who you truly are is deeper, more permanent, and bigger than any of these things. Who you truly are doesn't depend upon when or where you were born or the name you were given at birth to be happy, content, confident, and at peace. Notice who you truly are before these things.

Your falling has stopped.

You have now reached bottom.

There is just a pitch-black emptiness. There is nothing here but empty, open, clear, and honest awareness. From here on out, you will always have the capability, strength, and courage to recognize who you truly are—without any thing, person, place, time, or experience defining, limiting, stopping, preventing, changing, or altering you. You have dismantled and let go of your identity as a separate you...as a separate ego.

You now begin rising up out of the deep dark ravine. Faster and faster you rise. The rushing air begins again. Sound returns.

Feeling states return. Soon you begin to see the faint glimmer of light. Slowly, shadows form and you can make out the cliff wall as you ascend.

Faster and faster you rise. The light becomes stronger. Rising and rising. You ascend the canyon ravine. You see the colors of the cliff wall rush by you in a blur.

You can now see the sky. And now you can see the cliff edge far above you. Rising, rising. It is now fully light again. The cliff edge gets closer. You rise further and further until, at last, you reach the cliff edge.

You land...whole, at peace, empty...and stand next to me.

Lesson 27:
Free Fall

Listen

Spiritual Badass Homework:

Grab your journal and scribble out a few answers:

- Describe how you were feeling before The Freefall Exercise.
- Describe how you were feeling after The Freefall Exercise.
- Do you still feel it now?
- Has anything changed about who you think you are?
- What was the hardest part of you to let go of during The Freefall Exercise?
- Who are you?

Why do this?

Finding out who you really are, experiencing it, and then letting your hand scribe out the truth of it can be profound and life changing. Allow yourself to automatically write. In other words—don't think about it. Scribble it! Shout it on paper! Puke it up and out! Tell the truth! Be brutal! Be honest! It will do you wonders.

Notes:

LESSON 28
SEEING EXTERNAL EGO

How to let go of external things

This exercise should and is intended to elicit the "sobering truth" response in you. In other words, it should sting a little, and that sting usually shows up as a deep sadness, heaviness, or short-lived depressed state. This is exactly the ego-dismantling process. That's your ego sobering up and realizing some shit about itself that it didn't really want to realize. And it's good medicine. Actually, it's great fucking medicine.

Reading this will elicit the sobering truth, but listening to it will call it out powerfully and quickly.

The Seeing Ego Externally Exercise:

Time required: 30-45 minutes

Preparation: Find a comfortable quiet space where you won't be disturbed. It's best to *remain seated* for this one—in a relaxed, comfortable position.

Task: Below is the script for reading and sharing *Seeing Ego Externally Exercise*. Read it here first to familiarize yourself with it. Then listen to the audio or get together with a friend or relative and share it. If you're a teacher or guide, you can read the script to your class.

Three Deep Breaths: Begin by taking three deep breaths so that you learn with *both* body and mind.

1. Take a large inhale followed by a large exhale.

2. Take a second large inhale followed by a large exhale.
3. Take a third large inhale followed by a large exhale.

Briefly tune into the current state of the body:
Pay attention to the general state of the body—tired, achy, hungry, relaxed, excited, hopeful, agitated, nervous, concerned, or perhaps not feeling much of anything. Allow everything to be as it is.

Brief Body Scan:
Place awareness on your body...
Notice your Toes, Feet, Ankles, Shins, Knees, Thighs. *Breathe deeply.* Notice your Groin, Lower Back, Stomach, Mid-Chest, Heart, Upper Back. *Breathe deeply.* Notice your Shoulders, Arms, Elbows, Hands, Fingers. *Breathe deeply.* Notice your Neck, Face, Forehead, Scalp, Top of the Head. *Breathe deeply.*

Place your attention and awareness on your whole being during this exercise. As you listen to the words I'm about to communicate, let them resonate in your heart and body. Breathe deeply. If you feel resistance to these words—notice the resistance, allow it, embrace it, and let it go. Resistance is completely normal, natural, and okay. Simply see that you are not the resistance—you are not the fear. You are the awareness that precedes and perceives the fear and the resistance.

Seeing Ego in The Universe

The Universe is infinite, which makes it a realm—not a place. And just like a dream, the Universe has no edges or boundaries in time or space. The primary law in the Universe is this: For every action, there is an equal and opposite reaction. This is the first law of thermodynamics and in Oriental philosophy, the Tao. What this law means for you is that no matter how hard you try or how sophisticated your efforts are, ego will never attain complete fulfillment.

The Universe is limited and conditional. There has never been a time in this Universe when complete ego fulfillment was possible. There will never *be* a time. Simply put, this entire Universe is a *learning* realm. It will never be the paradise that ego promises.

Release the fantasy that the world—the Universe—will someday in the future be a perfect paradise. Release the delusion that life in the past, either a hundred years or a thousand years ago, was somehow better. Release the delusion that life in the future will somehow be better.

The Universe and the laws that govern it will always be the same. Release the Universe as a place to gain fulfillment. Relax and embrace the Universe as a dream realm and, paradoxically, you will awaken to the fulfillment you were seeking.

Think of the Universe now; be aware and mindful while you are doing this. Lovingly let it go. Lovingly see and feel how this Universe fails to truly fulfill.

Who are you before the Universe? Who are you after the Universe? Who are you now?

Seeing Ego in The World and Society

The world—along with the people who inhabit it, the governments which run it, and the ideologies which guide it— is an imperfect place. There is no perfect country. No perfect policy. No perfect government. No perfect political party. No perfect society. No perfect religion. No perfect philosophy. No perfect spirituality. No perfect race, skin color, tribe, ethnicity, or way of life. All of it is limited. All of it is conditional. Ego demands certain conditions for fulfillment to occur. Ego demands the right country, the right political party, the right president, the right religion, the right church, town, time, and place to be fulfilled.

Let this go. There is great wisdom in allowing the world to be exactly the way it is: seemingly imperfect, flawed, and broken. Paradoxically, it is when we let go of our efforts to control, manipulate, enforce, coerce, improve, or change the world that it becomes a better, lighter, and freer place—that *we* become better, lighter, and freer.

Let the world go and you will awaken to the fulfillment you were seeking all along. Think of the world and society now—be aware and mindful while you are doing this. Lovingly let them go. Lovingly see and feel how the world and society have failed to truly fulfill.

Who are you before the world? After the world? Who are you now?

Seeing Ego in Family and Friends

Seeing ego in family and friends means that you begin to see all of the ways in which your ego identity project is grasping, clinging, manipulating, and seeking fulfillment through those with whom you are most intimate.

Perhaps you are seeking to have your parents understand, respect, or admire you. Perhaps you are longing for your siblings to be more like you. Perhaps your cousins need to act more responsibly. Perhaps your husband does not listen or your wife does not participate. For ego—there is always something wrong with family, something that needs changing, improving, or fixing. Ego never accepts them just the way they are. Ego does the same with friends.

There is no perfect parent. There is no perfect grandparent, brother, sister, aunt, uncle, or cousin. There is no perfect family. There is no perfect friend, friendship, or group of friends. Our families and friends are limited—flawed and imperfect. Seeing ego in family and friends implicates all.

Upon seeing your ego, you begin to see the ego of others—including family and friends. You soon begin to see that all egos are simply doing the best they can. They, too, are seeking and longing for fulfillment and love. With this seeing comes great compassion and the truest understanding of human nature."

Let your family and friends go and, paradoxically, you will awaken to the fulfillment you were seeking through them all along. Think of your family and friends now—be aware and mindful while you are doing this. Lovingly let them go. Lovingly see and feel how family and friends have failed to truly fulfill.

Who are you before family and friends? Who are you after family and friends? Who are you now?

Seeing Ego in Sexuality

Seeing ego in sexuality means seeing the failure of sex to bring true lasting fulfillment. Seeing ego in sex is simply seeing the limitation of sex and accepting it. Seeing ego in sex is to let go of our neurotic, grasping, and never-ending desire for fulfillment though sex.

Let me be very clear here: There is nothing inherently wrong with sex. Sex is not bad. But it is very common for egos to rely solely on sex for fulfillment. Seeing ego in sex is to release it from the bonds of this unrealistic fulfillment expectation.

There is no perfect sex. No perfect sexual partner. No perfect amount of sex. No perfect place for sex. No perfect kind or form of sex.

Let sex go and, paradoxically, you will awaken to the fulfillment you were seeking through sex all along. Think of sex now—be aware and mindful while you are doing this. Lovingly let it go. Lovingly see and feel how sex has failed to truly fulfill.

Who are you before sex? After sex? Who are you now?

233

Seeing Ego in Work and Play

Seeing ego in work means seeing the failure of a career, work, or job to bring true lasting fulfillment. Seeing ego in work is simply seeing the limitation of work and accepting it. Seeing ego in work is to let go of seeking fulfillment through work.

There is no perfect job, work, or career. No perfect place to work. No perfect time to work. No perfect boss. No perfect employees. No perfect co-workers. No perfect salary. No perfect hourly rate. No perfect monetary compensation.

Work does not ultimately fulfill. Work is conditional.

Seeing ego in play means seeing the failure of a hobby, pastime, or passion to bring true lasting fulfillment. Seeing ego in play is simply seeing the limitation of play and accepting it. Seeing ego in play is to let go of seeking fulfillment through play. There is no perfect hobby, pastime, or passion. No perfect sport. No perfect art. No perfect project. No perfect creativity. No perfect movie, book, play, festival, or party.

Let work and play go and, paradoxically, you will awaken to the fulfillment you were seeking through work and play. Think of work and play now—be aware and mindful while you are doing this. Lovingly let it go. Lovingly see and feel how work and play have failed to truly fulfill.

Who are you before work and play? After work and play? Who are you now?

Listen

Spiritual Badass Homework:

Grab your journal and scribble out a few answers:

- What was your feeling of the sobering truth in this exercise?
- Which external ego part stung the most?
- Do you still feel it now?
- Has anything changed about who you think you are?
- Who are you before external ego?

Why do this?

I'll repeat this because it's worth it: Finding out who you really are, experiencing it, and then letting your hand scribe out the truth of it can be profound and life changing. Allow yourself to automatically write. In other words—don't think about it. Scribble it! Shout it on paper! Puke it up and out! Tell the truth! Be brutal! Be honest! It will do you wonders.

Notes:

Notes:

LESSON 29
SEEING INTERNAL EGO

How to let go of internal things

We'll now focus on seeing ego internally. We focus on the things we do with our head and heart: eating, talking, thinking, and emoting. The process of seeing ego in these activities is no different from the process of seeing ego in the universe, the world, our families, friends, sexuality, and work. We simply need to get real about the fulfillment these activities truly provide. We need to see the difference between the normal and natural qualities of these activities and the negative and neurotic qualities.

Eating, talking, thinking, and emoting are fine when you are hungry, need to speak to someone, need to figure something out, feel scared about the car that just nearly hit you, excited about the game you just won, or sad about the relative who passed away. But when eating, talking, thinking, and emoting become the sole cure for our existential spiritual ache, we get in trouble. When we eat, talk, think, and worry as a reaction to an underlying stress or unhappiness, it only compounds the problem. We are now adding unhappiness and suffering to our unhappiness and suffering—and most of us do this unconsciously. Most of us are not mindful or aware that we are using these activities as a shallow substitute for true fulfillment.

I'll repeat what I stated about the last exercise—*Seeing Ego External*: This exercise should and is intended to elicit the "sobering truth" response in you. It should sting a little, and that sting usually shows up as a deep sadness, heaviness, or short-lived depressed state. This is exactly the ego-dismantling process. That's your ego sobering up and realizing some shit about itself that it didn't really want to realize...

239

Reading this will elicit the sobering truth. *Listening* to it will call it out powerfully and quickly.

The Seeing Ego Internally Exercise:

Time required: 30-45 minutes

Preparation: Find a comfortable quiet space where you won't be disturbed. It's best to *remain seated* for this one—in a relaxed, comfortable position.

Task: Below is the script for reading and sharing *Seeing Ego Internally Exercise*. Read it here first to familiarize yourself with it. Then listen to the audio or get together with a friend or relative and share it. If you're a teacher or guide, you can read the script to your class.

Three Deep Breaths: Begin by taking three deep breaths so that you learn with *both* body and mind.

1. Take a large inhale followed by a large exhale.
2. Take a second large inhale followed by a large exhale.
3. Take a third large inhale followed by a large exhale.

Briefly tune into the current state of the body:
Pay attention to the general state of the body—tired, achy, hungry, relaxed, excited, hopeful, agitated, nervous, concerned, or perhaps not feeling much of anything. Allow everything to be as it is.

Brief Body Scan:
Place awareness on your body...
Notice your Toes, Feet, Ankles, Shins, Knees, Thighs. *Breathe deeply*. Notice your Groin, Lower Back, Stomach, Mid-Chest, Heart, Upper Back. *Breathe deeply*. Notice your Shoulders, Arms, Elbows, Hands, Fingers. *Breathe deeply*. Notice your Neck, Face, Forehead, Scalp, Top of the Head. *Breathe deeply*.

Place your attention and awareness on your whole being during this exercise. As you listen to the words I'm about to communicate, let them resonate in your heart and body. Breathe deeply. If you feel resistance to these words—notice the resistance, allow it, embrace it, and let it go. Resistance is completely normal, natural, and okay. Simply see that you are not the resistance—you are not the fear. You are the awareness that precedes and perceives the fear and the resistance.

Seeing Ego in Rich Foods

Cake, pies, muffins, cookies, ice cream, candy, sugared cereals, Coke, fruit drinks, and more.

See the element of ego which seeks fulfillment through rich foods. There's nothing evil or bad about rich foods, but when chocolate cake is covering up or numbing the hole in your heart or spirit, it must be seen.

Lovingly be aware of the ego activity of rich foods. Allow awareness to see the ego activity of rich foods.

Who are you before eating rich foods? After rich foods? Who are you now?

Seeing Ego in Normal Foods

Oatmeal, orange juice, cereal, eggs, ham, toast, salad, turkey, fish, broccoli, rice, pasta, tomatoes, peppers, eggplant, chicken, bananas, apples, an occasional frozen meal or fast-food meal, and more.

See the element of ego which seeks fulfillment through normal foods. You obviously have to eat. But when eating even normal foods is covering up or numbing the hole in your heart or spirit, it must be seen.

Lovingly be aware of the ego activity of normal foods Allow awareness to see the ego activity of normal foods.

Who are you before eating? After eating? Who are you now?

Seeing Ego in Toxic Stuff

Alcohol, beer, wine, cigarettes, cigars, marijuana, vapes, tobacco dip, numbing pharmaceuticals, hard drugs like crystal meth, and more.

See the element of ego which seeks fulfillment through toxic stuff. Certain toxic stuff is fine—in moderation. Other toxic stuff is not fine under any circumstance. Your job is to see that toxic stuff is usually covering up or numbing a hole in your heart or spirit.

Lovingly be aware of the ego activity of toxic stuff. Who are you before toxic stuff? After toxic stuff? Who are you now? Allow awareness to see the ego activity of toxic stuff.

Seeing Ego in Positive Emotions

Love, happiness, joy, laughter, serenity, peace, confidence, admiration, trust, acceptance, anticipation, interest, passion, and more.

See the element of ego which seeks fulfillment through positive emotions. Obviously, nothing wrong with positive emotions, but, oddly enough, positive emotions can also be used to mask, hide, or numb deeper internal issues.

Lovingly be aware of the ego activity of positive emotions. Allow awareness to see the ego activity of positive emotions.

Who are you before positive emotions? After positive emotions? Who are you now?

Seeing Ego in Negative Emotions

Anger, rage, loathing, grief, terror, disgust, sadness, fear, annoyance, boredom, distraction, denial, remorse, and more.

See the element of ego which seeks fulfillment through negative emotions. Negative emotions serve a valid purpose. Often, however, we slip into overindulging in negative emotions. Negative emotions very often hide, mask, numb, and prevent us from seeing deeper existential or spiritual holes.

Lovingly be aware of the ego activity of negative emotions. Allow awareness to see the ego activity of negative emotions.

Who are you before negative emotions? After negative emotions? Who are you now?

Seeing Ego in Indulgent Talking

Rambling, storytelling, exaggeration, dramatization, repetition, veering way off topic, getting lost in minutia, not taking social cues, talking without listening, controlling, demanding, sucking energy, and more.

See the element of ego which seeks fulfillment through indulgent talking. We've all been here before: The person with whom you are talking is not listening, not paying attention, and is chattering on and on. This is indulgent talking. Nine times out of ten, indulgent talking is burying or numbing hidden pain, old unconscious wounds, or a deeply unheard and unseen heart.

Lovingly be aware of the ego activity of indulgent talking. Allow awareness to see the ego activity of indulgent talking.

Who are you before indulgent talking? After indulgent talking? Who are you now?

Seeing Ego in Practical Talking

Small talk, deep conversation, normal conversation, directions, help, assistance, guidance, joking, storytelling, reminiscing, touching base, just saying hi, and more.

See the element of ego which seeks fulfillment through practical talking. We all have to communicate and talk, but ego is always present, even in day-to-day normal talking. Ego is always seeking, longing, wanting, and needing.

Lovingly be aware of the ego activity of practical talking Allow awareness to see the ego activity of practical talking.

Who are you before practical talking? After practical talking? Who are you now?

Seeing Ego in Thoughts and Thinking

Every single thought you've ever had, will ever have in the future, and/or are currently having is infiltrated by ego. *Every single thought. All of them.*

Allow awareness to see and notice all thoughts...high or low, good or bad, dull or amazing, banal or insightful. Your brain is a chronic thought-processing me, me, me-machine that never stops. All you can do is become *aware* of these thoughts. Do this and most thoughts lose their umph, bite, or toxic quality.

Lovingly be aware of the ego activity of thoughts and thinking. Allow awareness to see the ego activity of thoughts and thinking.

Who are you before thinking? After thinking? Who are you now?

Lesson 29:
Seeing Internal Ego

Listen

Grab your journal and jot down a few answers:

- What was your feeling of the sobering truth in this exercise?
- Which internal ego part stung the most?
- Do you still feel it now?
- Has anything changed about who you think you are?
- Who are you before internal ego?

Why do this?

You know why: Healing the inside often requires that we bring it into the light of day—on the outside. Allow yourself to automatically write. In other words—don't think about it. Scribble it! Shout it on paper! Puke it up and out! Tell the truth! Be brutal! Be honest! It will do you wonders.

Notes:

Notes:

LESSON 30
TATTOO THERAPY

How to heal and love yourself

In Chapter Twenty-four of *Spirituality for Badasses Book 1*, I introduce you to Brent, the owner and operator of *Dr. Feel Good's Tattoos*. (Remember that he had been a psychotherapist earlier in his life.) While visiting, you collapse into a teary-eyed mess as you recall an early childhood incident involving your now deceased uncle. Brent graciously takes you into his office, with J., Lenny, and Tenzin in tow, and invites you to have a "therapy" session. The therapy you receive is in no way, shape, or form conventional western psychotherapy. It's actually a mash-up of *Mindfulness-Based Cognitive Therapy* and *Somato Emotional Release Therapy*, both of which I used during my own spiritual badass journey, and both of which I use in just about every aspect of my work as an author and teacher.

You've actually *already* been learning and practicing *Mindfulness-Based Cognitive Therapy* and *Somato Emotional Release Therapy* both in this workbook and in Book 1. It's not rocket science. It works like this: Meet it. Greet it. Feel it. Love it. Let it go. Bang. You're done. Of course, there are deeper principles at work—primarily your ability to be acutely aware and conscious *while* you meet, greet, feel, love, and let go.

So, here's the deal and then I'll stop getting all therapy-science on your ass: *You're ready for this.* Everything you've done so far (assuming you have *actually* done it) has prepared you: You're attentive. You're aware. You're mindful. You know what

249

the limitations of ego are. And now it's time to deal with your shit. It's time for some Tattoo Therapy...

But, but, but...

I can hear your arguments three and a half miles away. If you seriously think you don't have any shit to deal with—you are deluding yourself. It's either buried, lost, forgotten, walled off, numbed, or totally denied. Trust me friend, *everyone's* got shit to deal with.

What is your wound? *When* was your wound? What is your trauma? *When* was your trauma? What is your pain? *When* was your pain? These are some questions we're going to go deep into during this exercise.

I'm not going to bullshit you: *Mindfulness-Based Cognitive Therapy* and *Somato Emotional Release Therapy* are best done in private and with an actual real, live, certified and trained human being. But here we are, so, we'll make do given the circumstances.

The Tattoo Therapy Exercise:

Time required: 30-45 minutes

Preparation: Find a comfortable quiet space where you won't be disturbed. You can be seated or lying down in a relaxed, comfortable position for this one.

Task: Below is the script for reading and sharing the *Tattoo Therapy Exercise*. Read it here first to familiarize yourself with it. Then listen to the audio or get together with a friend or relative and share it. If you're a teacher or guide, you can read the script to your class.

Three Deep Breaths: Begin by taking three deep breaths so that you learn with *both* body and mind.

1. Take a large inhale followed by a large exhale.
2. Take a second large inhale followed by a large exhale.
3. Take a third large inhale followed by a large exhale.

Briefly tune into the current state of the body:
Pay attention to the general state of the body—tired, achy, hungry, relaxed, excited, hopeful, agitated, nervous, concerned, or perhaps not feeling much of anything. Allow everything to be as it is.

Brief Body Scan:
Place awareness on your body...
Notice your Toes, Feet, Ankles, Shins, Knees, Thighs. *Breathe deeply.* Notice your Groin, Lower Back, Stomach, Mid-Chest, Heart, Upper Back. *Breathe deeply.* Notice your Shoulders, Arms, Elbows, Hands, Fingers. *Breathe deeply.* Notice your Neck, Face, Forehead, Scalp, Top of the Head. *Breathe deeply.*

The Wounded Toddler

Maybe you were wounded or traumatized as toddler...

Do your best to recall the wound, the trauma, and the ensuing pain it caused when you were a toddler.

Recall how it felt emotionally.

Locate the pain in your body *right now.*

Allow the pain and emotion to be completely present.

Now is the time to stop pushing it away or denying it.

Invite it all the way in...here and now.

Allow whatever part of the body holding the pain to clench, tighten, burn, tense—whatever the response—completely and fully.

Breathe and be aware.

Notice the one who is experiencing the pain; the one who is noticing the pain.

Try to be as present as you can—and allow the pain of that event, of that time, when you were a toddler, to be here right now. Welcome it all here.

Every crappy situation, every painful circumstance...has two sides. Every wound has both a pain and a gift. You've certainly received *both* the pain and the gift. The toddler received both the pain and the gift.

We're not trying to fix or change your past. But we can find the toddler who is—believe it or not—still with you *as this wound*. And with awareness, we can acknowledge the toddler, see the toddler, thank the toddler, hold the toddler, love the toddler, and let that little person go.

Can you do this?

That little person did the best he or she could. That little person made you who you are today.

Breathe...cry...emote

The Wounded Child

Maybe you were wounded or traumatized as a young child...

Do your best to recall the wound, the trauma and the ensuing pain it caused when you were a child.

Recall how it felt emotionally.

Locate the pain in your body *right now*.

Allow the pain and emotion to be completely present.

Now is the time to stop pushing it away or denying it.

Invite it all the way in... here and now.

Allow whatever part of the body holding the pain to clench, tighten, burn, tense—whatever the response—completely and fully.

Breathe and be aware.

Notice the one who is experiencing the pain; the one who is noticing the pain.

Try to be as present as you can—and allow the pain of that event, of that time, when you were a child, to be here right now. Welcome it all here.

Every crappy situation, every painful circumstance...has two sides. Every wound has both a pain and a gift. You've certainly received *both* the pain and the gift. The child received both the pain and the gift.

We're not trying to fix or change your past. But we can find the child who is—believe it or not—still with you *as this wound*. And with awareness, we can acknowledge the child, see the child, thank the child, hold the child, love the child, and let that little child go.

Can you do this?

That little child did the best he or she could. That little child made you who you are today.

Breathe and emote.

The Wounded Teenager

Maybe you were wounded or traumatized as a teenager...

Do your best to recall the wound, the trauma and the ensuing pain it caused when you were a teenager.

Recall how it felt emotionally.

Locate the pain in your body *right now.*

Allow the pain and emotion to be completely present.

Now is the time to stop pushing it away or denying it.

Invite it all the way in... here and now.

Allow whatever part of the body holding the pain to clench, tighten, burn, tense—whatever the response—completely and fully.

Breathe and be aware.

Notice the one who is experiencing the pain; the one who is noticing the pain.

Try to be as present as you can—and allow the pain of that event, of that time, when you were a teenager, to be here right now. Welcome it all here.

Every crappy situation, every painful circumstance...has two sides. Every wound has both a pain and a gift. You've certainly received *both* the pain and the gift. The teenager received both the pain and the gift.

We're not trying to fix or change your past. But we can find the teenager who is—believe it or not—still with you *as this wound.* And with awareness, we can acknowledge the teenager, see the teenager, thank the teenager, hold the teenager, love the teenager, and let that teenager go.

Can you do this?

That teenager did the best he or she could. That teenager made you who you are today.

Breathe and emote.

The Wounded Young Adult

Maybe you were wounded or traumatized as a young adult...

Do your best to recall the wound, the trauma and the ensuing pain it caused when you were a young adult.

Recall how it felt emotionally.

Locate the pain in your body *right now.*

Allow the pain and emotion to be completely present.

Now is the time to stop pushing it away or denying it.

Invite it all the way in... here and now.

Allow whatever part of the body holding the pain to clench, tighten, burn, tense—whatever the response—completely and fully.

Breathe and be aware.

Notice the one who is experiencing the pain; the one who is noticing the pain.

Try to be as present as you can—and allow the pain of that event, of that time, when you were a young adult, to be here right now. Welcome it all here.

Every crappy situation, every painful circumstance...has two sides. Every wound has both a pain and a gift. You've certainly received *both* the pain and the gift. The young adult received both the pain and the gift.

We're not trying to fix or change your past. But we can find the young adult who is—believe it or not—still with you *as this wound*. And with awareness, we can acknowledge the young adult, see the young adult, thank the young adult, hold the young adult, love the young adult, and let that young adult go.

Can you do this?

That young adult did the best he or she could. That young adult made you who you are today.

Breathe and emote.

The Wounded Adult

Maybe you were wounded or traumatized as an adult...

Do your best to recall the wound, the trauma and the ensuing pain it caused.

Recall how it felt emotionally.

Locate the pain in your body *right now.*

Allow the pain and emotion to be completely present.

Now is the time to stop pushing it away or denying it.

Invite it all the way in... here and now.

Allow whatever part of the body holding the pain to clench, tighten, burn, tense—whatever the response—completely and fully.

Breathe and be aware.

Notice the one who is experiencing the pain; the one who is noticing the pain.

Try to be as present as you can—and allow the pain of that event, of that time, to be here right now. Welcome it all here.

Every crappy situation, every painful circumstance...has two sides. Every wound has both a pain and a gift. You've certainly received *both* the pain and the gift.

We're not trying to fix or change your past. But we can find the adult who is—believe it or not—still with you *as this wound.* And with awareness, we can acknowledge the adult, see the adult, thank the adult, hold the adult, love the adult and let that adult go.

Can you do this?

That adult did the best he or she could. That adult made you who you are today.

Breathe and emote.

Lesson 30:
Tattoo Therapy

Listen

Spiritual Badass Homework:

Grab your journal and scribble out a few answers:

- At what age did you experience a wound or trauma?
- How did you feel and respond during this exercise?
- Were you able to "Meet it. Greet it. Feel it. Love it. Let it go." ?
- Do you still feel any residual effects from the exercise?
- Has anything changed about the present you or the past you?
- Who are you in this very moment?

Why do this?

Healing our past is a very important part of the art of living in the present. In order to fully live in the present, we must do so without the baggage, regret, deep wounds or weight from our past. You can't change the past—but you can change *the current part of you* that is still stuck and wounded from the past.

Notes:

LESSON 31
RIDING ROLLERCOASTERS

How to meet deep fear

There are really only two things you can do when you encounter a large amount of existential internal fear: Say yes to awareness and say yes to fear.

Chapter Twenty-five of *Spirituality for Badasses Book 1* culminates at *Carowinds* amusement park, where you have to do just this: The aftereffects of a rollercoaster ride have caused an existential crisis where you are forced to meet a large amount of internal fear that you'd been avoiding. When you finally allow the fear to overcome you through saying yes to awareness and fear, you pass out...and wake up feeling lighter, unburdened, and greatly relieved.

All of this is easier said than done. And, sorry—there is no exercise I can give you that is going to elicit an existential panic attack that, should you choose to embrace, would provide instant healing, wholeness, or ultra-spiritual cosmic enlightenment. *It just don't work that way.* Fear comes on its own terms, usually when you least expect it, and—good news— usually when you're ready to handle it.

So yeah, sorry—no specific exercise for this one, but here's what I can do: I can inspire you and empower you with courage by sharing two pivotal experiences of my own spiritual badass journey. (I actually shared a version of these in my first book, *21 Days: A Guide for Spiritual Beginners*) You can read them or listen to them, allowing my experiences to sink deep into your skin and then—when it's your turn—at least you'll have had some preparation. Sound good? (Rhetorical question. I know you have no choice, but I like to be gentlemanly once in a blue moon.)

Okay. Well, I guess we *will* approach this like an exercise. Here we go...

Deep Fear Exercise:

Time required: 10-15 minutes

Preparation: Find a comfortable quiet space where you won't be disturbed. You can be seated or lying down in a relaxed, comfortable position for this one.

Task: Below is the script for reading and sharing the *Deep Fear Exercise*. Read it here first to familiarize yourself with it. Then listen to the audio or get together with a friend or relative and share it. If you're a teacher or guide, you can read the script to your class.

Three Deep Breaths: Begin by taking three deep breaths so that you learn with *both* body and mind.

1. Take a large inhale followed by a large exhale.
2. Take a second large inhale followed by a large exhale.
3. Take a third large inhale followed by a large exhale.

Briefly tune into the current state of the body:

Pay attention to the general state of the body—tired, achy, hungry, relaxed, excited, hopeful, agitated, nervous, concerned, or perhaps not feeling much of anything. Allow everything to be as it is.

Brief Body Scan:

Place awareness on your body...

Notice your Toes, Feet, Ankles, Shins, Knees, Thighs. *Breathe deeply.* Notice your Groin, Lower Back, Stomach, Mid-Chest, Heart, Upper Back. *Breathe deeply.* Notice your Shoulders, Arms, Elbows, Hands, Fingers. *Breathe deeply.* Notice your Neck, Face, Forehead, Scalp, Top of the Head. *Breathe deeply.*

J. Stewart Dixon Experience One

It's December 19th, 1997.

It's movie time. I'm driving around the shopping district with my friend Miles at about 10 P.M. We were just in Borders Books purchasing a few Christmas presents. Time to kill. I suggest we go see a movie. This was back in the day when, if you wanted to know what time a movie began, you either called the theater (with dubious results) or you just got in your car and drove. We drive. I pop out of the car and run into the theater while Miles waits. 11 P.M.—that's when it starts. Cool. We go park the car and then scurry through the biting cold air into a loud, bustling, over-crowded cineplex. Bustling and overcrowded because, despite the fact that it's around 10:30 P.M., there is a national— soon to be international—movie-going phenomenon taking place. It's called *Titanic.*

I don't need to describe this movie to you. No doubt you've seen it, perhaps multiple times. It's James Cameron's then Christmas gift to the world. We grab some popcorn and drinks and go sit down in the theater. No previews. You know a movie is big when the movie studio forgoes bombarding you with advertisements for their other movies.

Fast forward to the part where the ship is sinking, and all aboard know that the inevitable is coming...

In a nutshell, *Titanic* is about death. I've been on the spiritual badass path for about six years now and if there's one thing I can tell you, it's this: Discovering your own internal spiritual badass is also, in a nutshell, about death. I won't explain the details of this, but it's not hard to imagine that in order to discover something of this magnitude, other things are gonna have to give way. Other things are going to have to die. Thus, during the search or path or adventure, one encounters in a very real way—over and over again—the wall of one's own mortality, characterized by encounters with existential fear: fear of death, fear of annihilation, fear of isolation, fear of failure, fear of unhappiness, etc. Pretty heavy stuff. *Titanic* is also about some pretty heavy stuff. On this movie-going night, there is a case where—against all odds—two objects with two different trajectories are going to collide. I'm not referring to the boat and the iceberg here. I'm referring to me and this movie.

The knot in my stomach started with the dancing scene in the engine room of the lower sections of the ship.

Something about that scene triggered a very real knowledge of my own impending death. *Existential* death, not physical death. Existential death points to the death of ingrained notions, ideas, delusions that you are a separate ghostly or disembodied entity trapped in a physical body and/or that you are a physical body trapped in the world. The true death of these ideas manifests with a tremendous amount of fear—and consequently feels very much like physical death.

I am now sweating and growing pale and faint with fear. A cold chill settles over my body. I've got the shakes. Dread has filled my entire being. What the hell have I done? Why did I go mucking around in these matters? What was I thinking? I've been diddling like a debutante in a whorehouse with the fabric of the universe and it's now about to unravel, taking me along with it. Tears of horror are forming in my eyeballs. I'm having trouble holding them back. I say something to Miles and stumble out of the theater. I walk on jelly legs to the exit and collapse to my knees out front. A few deep breaths of cold air. Miles follows. I'm crying now, garbling my words to Miles in an effort to explain. I'm not going back into the theater. Sorry— movie got to me. Death...he's understanding. We walk over to the car and get in. I'm a bundle of raw nerves. We head back to his place.

We arrive at Miles' apartment. I'm too fried to drive home, so I decide to spend the night. I lie down in the guest bedroom. I am still in the grip of a deep, dreadful existential fear. But for the first time, I take notice of something. I can literally feel awareness or consciousness moving across my brain, as if from the left hemisphere to the right hemisphere, as if for the first time spreading into new locations across my brain. I think to myself that this movement is the cause of all the fear. Knowing this doesn't alleviate the fear, but at least puts it into perspective. There's something biological about this mess I've gotten myself into and it's completely out of my control. It's going to run its course whether I like it or not. Might as well relax. Stop trying to control. Stop trying to manipulate. Stop putting it off. This resolution helps a little, but by and large the fear remains, and I sleep fitfully throughout the night.

It subsides by morning. I survive. I thank Miles for letting me spend the night and get in my car. During the drive home, I realize...this will not be the end of it. This was the biggest encounter I've ever had with this beast, but it will be back. This I'm sure of. At least...I think when it does come back, I will be able to handle it. I will have the courage to handle it. Yes—I will.

Take Another Three Deep Breaths:

1. Take a large inhale followed by a large exhale.
2. Take a second large inhale followed by a large exhale.
3. Take a third large inhale followed by a large exhale.

J. Stewart Dixon Experience Two

Two years later: It's 7 A.M., February 6, 1999.

I'm sick. Ugh. I have a terrible cough, and I need some cough medicine...

Only I don't have any cough medicine, and—much worse—I don't have any cash. Sounds like an easy problem to remedy; I know—ATM machine—but A) I have no money in my account, B) my bank has no local ATM machine, and C) my bank is a half hour away. The only thing I do have are several checks made out to the business I run. It's a small amount of money, but enough, certainly, to get the goods. All I have to do is drag my sorry ass out of bed, walk through the freezing cold, get into my car, and drive down the road. Not a thrilling prospect.

As I'm pondering this immensely inane situation, I have another coughing attack which serves as a cattle prod to stir my lazy and sickly bovine existence into action. I am now resolute in my determination to make the dreaded trip.

I quickly get dressed, bundle up, and walk out to the car. No sign of roommates—too early for them. I get in my car, start it up, and peel down the driveway.

I room with another guy and two girls. We're all around the same age. I'll be thirty this year. We live in an old farmhouse surrounded by about three hundred acres of state-designated park. Nice place to live. It's called Skylark Farm. We all love it and treat it like our own, even though we're just renters. I've been living here for about four years. I'm self-employed. My company is called *Sealife Aquarium Service.* I've been cleaning fish tanks for about five years. I hate it—primarily because I'm tired of slopping up fish shit; secondarily because I'm in the midst of negotiating the sale of the company, and I have one foot out the door; and lastly because about four months ago, I received a very partial grant to produce a big rock musical I wrote called *Magic Music Myth,* and I'd much rather be pursuing this. I am stewing a fetid pot of possibility, desire, ambition, hope, and fear. I have a lot on my mind. Most of what's on my mind, however, plays a depressing second fiddle to my coughing and hacking.

I make my way down a cold, misty, gray, and bleak highway. It's a torturous half-hour drive to the bank. My mind spins into delirium.

Getting closer. Sucks. Heavy heart. Who am I? Witness? Almost...bank. What am I doing? Feel like I'm in a bubble two thousand miles away. Who? Witnessing. If I . . .sell business . . .don't get rest of grant money. Show. Screwed.

Witnessing? Yes. Will have to get job. Just sell the damn business. Finally. Bank. Irritation, chest. Cough. Headache. Drive up window. Teller there. Thank God. Who am I? Roll window down. Hi. Morning. Cough. Checks, tube. Push button. Cash these, please. Who!. . . Who am I? Hold back cough. Roll up window. Headachy. Tired. Lot to do. Send out more faxes. Witness. Other aquarium services. Is that who I am? Hack. Hack. Come on. Money now, please. Awareness. Okay. Send it. Send it. Send it. What's the holdup? Cough. Cover mouth. Finally. Here comes. Who? . . . Roll down window. Take tube. Thanks. Am I the witness? Drive.

I speed out of the bank parking lot in a condition that would probably qualify me for a DUI, but luckily it's early Saturday morning—there's no fuzz around. I wind my way back down the road, coughing and stammering all the way. I drive to the local Walmart, enter, and make my way to the pharmacy section.

Grab the goods. Cough syrup. Hold back cough. Again . . . Who am I? The Witness. Checkout counter. One person ahead of me. Cough. Hand over mouth. Slightly dizzy. What's the holdup? Let's go. Let's go. Awareness. Feel like I'm in a bubble. Register broken. Okay, another register? Only one open. Got to be shitting me. Ugh. Come on! Damn it. Witnessing. Fuck this. Drop goods. Cough. Pissed off. Leave. Witness . . . Angry. Am I really angry? Walk to car. Start engine. No, not really. I'm witnessing the anger. Hack. Cough. Zip out of parking lot. Giant pharmacy just up block. Drive. Delirious. Witness? Arrive. Cough. Get out of car. Walk. Inside. Pharmacy section? Pharmacy? Got it. Walk. Grab goods. Cough syrup. Who am I? The hell with it. Open bottle now. Chug. Ahhh—yuck! Terrible shit. Register. Pay. Leave. Witness? Delirium. In a bubble. Cough. Drive home.

It's a quick, five-minute drive home. I pull into the driveway and, like a zombie, walk back into the house and up to my room. I'm the living dead. I lie down on my bed. I'm in a very strange space. I'm ripe for the universe to turn me inside out. I'm ripe for a very large chunk of ice to melt off, fall, and crush my existence into pieces. I'm ripe to meet the anti-maker. I'm ripe to meet FEAR. FEAR itself. Existential FEAR. The beast of all FEARS.

I wake up an hour or so later plagued by Sealife Aquarium Service and Magic Music Myth thoughts. I walk out to my office to do some paperwork. Send some faxes. Pay some bills. Worry. Stress. Contrive. Control. Last-ditch efforts to make something of my life.

It's coming, but I can't see it coming. It's good that it's a surprise. I would never go willingly. No one would. I'm an oblivious idiot puppet plaything, flitting in the wind of God's mercurial mind. I'm a discarded no-name object-thing. I'm a dusty worn-out toy about to be recycled. I work for several hours in my office. Late in the day now. The coughing returns. Time to chug some more medicine. And I do. It's a mistake. A good mistake. A very bad mistake.

I'm already in a disconnected, filmy, vague, discombobulated state, and the cough medicine adds no clarity. It takes me deeper into my hole. Primordial deep. Dark. Heavy. Black. Deep. I leave the office. I am the witness. I float over to the house. My roommate is in the kitchen. Witness. I talk with her. There is no Jeff talking. There's only the experience of talking. I am identified only as the witness. I am no longer Jeff. I am the witness experiencing Jeff. We talk. Pretend—like there is something important to say. Then . . .

Hello, Beast. My brain, heart, and body ignite with a fire of FEAR. DEATH. Now. Die. No avoiding it this time. The fear rumbles across my existence like a nuclear rocket down a dirt road. It looms on the horizon. I hear it coming for me. I politely leave my roommate. I walk upstairs to my bedroom. The FEAR rips apart my will, my efforts, my dreams, my control. It threatens to explode my life into a million pieces. I will let it. I am nobody. I am a dead man walking. Annihilate me. The full brunt of the nuclear explosion has yet to occur. I sit down on the bed. I gaze at the electrical outlet on the opposite wall. I take a deep breath. I am the Witness. I can handle this. Come now. Take me. It does.

I enter a space of fear beyond all imagination. I am seated in the center of a nuclear explosion. My heart pounds fiercely. Energy pours out my hands, lips, feet, and the top of my head— literal electrical voltage-like energy—at the speed of light. I am rattled to my utmost core. Nervous. Shaking. Wide-eyed. Every atom in my body feels as if it flips polarity. Every cell relaxes. Every muscle loosens. I die a thousand deaths. The release is beyond knowing, beyond bliss. It is acceptance—the final acceptance of loss. Loss of self. Loss of identity with self. I am the Witness now. I am the Consciousness behind all life. This is who I am. It ends. It has passed. It is finally over. No more running. No more hiding. Wall torn down. Block removed. Knot undone. I am free.

Lesson 31:
Deep Fear

Listen

Spiritual Badass Homework:

Grab your journal and scribble out a few answers:

- Have you ever experienced this kind of deep fear?
- How did you feel and respond during this exercise?
- Do you still feel any residual effects from the exercise?
- Do you think you have what it takes to meet deep fear?
- Can you say *yes* to awareness and *yes* to the fear?
- Who are you in this very moment?

Why do this?

The two yeses are more powerful than you can think or imagine. In the face of terrifying existential fear, it is *very* difficult to actually summon these two yeses. You will more than likely place your tail between your legs and run like a scared pooch. But—when your time comes, you'll know what to do.

I hope you've enjoyed riding rollercoasters with me. Don't be dismayed if your own journey doesn't unfold exactly as described in this lesson. It won't. You're *your own* unique badass and your rollercoaster adventure will be amazing and beautiful in its own unique way. I'll see you in the last exercise…

Notes:

Notes:

BONUS LESSON 32
CONGRATS!- I'LL DRINK TO THAT

How to drink tequila like a spiritual badass

Congratulations on finishing *The Workbook*! I sincerely hope you've had some insights, aha-moments, and spiritual badass realizations. May they benefit you *deeply and profoundly* for the rest of your life.

If you've made it to this lesson and have actually done all the others—well then, cheers! I'll drink to that! Mindfully, that is. You didn't think I'd actually write a workbook based on *Book 1* and not include a little *Mindful Tequila Drinking Exercise,* did you!?

Pleased to deliver: But—ain't no way I'm gonna write this one out. You gotta *experience* this one. You gotta join me at *Lucky's Two Stroke Biker Bar.*

So—grab a shot glass and a bottle of your favorite tequila and join me in the audio version of this exercise. Clearly, however—and I trust your spiritual badass to make this distinction and decision—if you've got problems with alcohol or addiction, *abstain from the alcohol.* It's totally cool to pour yourself a celebration seltzer. I'll do the tequila drinking. See you in the exercise.

Lesson 32:
Mindful Tequila

Listen

Spiritual Badass Homework:

Grab your journal and scribble out a few answers:

- Who are you before alcohol?
- Who are you during alcohol?
- Who are you after alcohol?
- Who are you with a hangover?
- Who are you in this very moment?

Why do this?

Spirituality for Badasses ain't done to benefit you while you're living under a rock or in a cave or vacationing in a cushy Caribbean meditation retreat. It's *real* world. Real ups. Real downs. Real highs. Real lows. Real experiences. We ain't saints, monks, or nuns. We're *Spiritual Badasses*—and it's okay to celebrate that with a shot of tequila (or two or three or four) once in a blue moon.

Notes:

EGO LETTER

Handwrite Me a Letter

Handwrite me a letter about your experience with *Spirituality for Badasses The Workbook Part Four: Ego Lessons. Your letter will be 100% private and not shared.* I've provided a list of questions below you can use as a guide, or write whatever moves you.

Why do this?

Writing out your deepest thoughts, fears, confessions, and internal dialogues will be very helpful for your spiritual badass journey. *It will get you there quicker.* Writing, sharing, or confessing *to someone* gets it out of *you* and into the light of day, where it can heal, transform, and benefit. Also—writing by hand is better. We tend to be more honest with a pen in hand.

Ego Letter Questions:

- Can you report any changes, aha-moments, or difficulties from the ego exercises in this part?
- What was the hardest part of ego to let go for you?
- How did the Tattoo Therapy Exercise affect you?
- Any wounds or traumas you had to revisit?
- How did the Deep Fear Exercise affect you?
- Have you ever had an existential fear panic attack?
- What did you learn about yourself in this part that you didn't know before?
- What did you learn about ego in this part that you didn't know before?
- How's life?

Send it here:

PIE Publishing c/o J. Stewart Dixon
P.O. Box 32
Earlysville VA 22936

END OF THE WORKBOOK

Congrats! Now that you've completed *The Workbook* continue your adventure with author J. Stewart Dixon.

Get Access to:
New Book Sneak Previews,
Online Courses, Videos, Humor,
Spiritual Badass Wisdom &
Swear Words for all.

Go here:
www.spiritualityforbadasses.com

AUDIO FILES
INSTRUCTIONS & LINK

Audio Files Access:

Go to this link to access
the free audio files that
accompany this book:

www.spiritualityforbadasses.com/sfbworkbook325

Prefer VIDEO? You're in luck.
Once you've gained access to the
free audio files there's an option
to upgrade to video.

Spirituality for Badasses blossomed out of J. Stewart's life as a spiritual seeker, finder, and teacher. He teaches based on his direct experience, twenty-nine years of interaction with numerous nonduality-advaita-zen-unorthodox teachers, his ongoing education / certification in modern mindfulness, and a degree in communications/engineering from Syracuse University.

Spirituality for Badasses is a #1 best-selling book in nine categories on Amazon. It won two top awards in the 2021 Global Book Awards: First prize for new age spirituality; Second prize for philosophy.

J. Stewart Dixon is a frequent media guest heard on national radio, podcasts, and YouTube channels. He has been a featured expert on SiriusXM Radio, iHeart Media, Audacy, Radio America, Buddha at the Gas Pump, and more.

His first book, *21 Days, A Guide for Spiritual Beginners* (2011, PIE Publishing / Amazon), continues to help beginning spiritual seekers worldwide.

Review, share & shout:

Your friends will be jealous you discovered this book before they did! They're gonna love it *and* you're gonna get some serious badass friend points. Help get the word out: Review it. Share it. Recommend it.

Things you can do

Write a review:
Make your world a more spiritual badass place. After reading, please leave a review with your thoughts, opinions, and stars. Just search *Amazon* for **Spirituality for Badasses The Workbook** and spread the love, baby.

Snap a photo & share:
Snap a photo of you and your copy of the book. Write a few words about it and share it on Facebook, Instagram, Twitter, and other social media sites.

Share your review or photo with me:
Spirituality for Badasses is on Facebook. Drop me a line and share your thoughts or photos of you with the book.

Buy an extra copy to give away:
Buy an extra copy and keep it in your car. Save it to give to the perfect person—and change the world, one spiritual badass at a time…

Fist Bump & Thank You!
J. Stewart Dixon

References

Dixon, J. Stewart. 2021.
Spirituality for Badasses
PIE Publishing / Awakening Resources, LLC

Dixon, J. Stewart. 2010.
21 Days: A Guide for Spiritual Beginners
PIE Publishing / Awakening Resources, LLC

Goleman, Daniel. 1994 / 2012.
Emotional Intelligence: Why It Can Matter More Than IQ
Bantam Books

Singer, Michael A. 2007.
The Untethered Soul
New Harbinger Publications/ Noetic Books

Enjoy...

Chapter 1
Jumper Nine, Go!

How to unlock your heart and soul

Say yes to awareness, yes to the fear.

Yes to awareness, yes to the fear.

You got this.

Two yeses.

You got...

The 52' 400 Series DHC-6 Twin Otter aircraft has reached jumping altitude—13,500 feet to be exact. You're strapped to your tandem skydive guide, Josh, seated on a customized, ten-foot long, silver aluminum bench that extends to the carpeted sliding hatch bay door jump area. Another jumper grabs the bay door and lifts, and like the snarling maw of a leviathan about to devour you, it opens. The rushing sound of wind, fury, fierceness, and nail-biting fear engulfs the cabin. Your palms sweat profusely. Your heart rate ticks up to maximum. Your nerve ganglia fire off a last-minute barrage of warning signals begging you to stop this insanity—

Oh, fuck. Oh, fuck.

Two yeses.

Can't believe I...agreed to this.

There's no going back now. You and the ten other jumpers are committed. And *yes: You agreed to this shit. But* it's not the skydiving you can't believe you agreed to.

Jumper one—go!

Jumper two—go!

You watch as they jump and tumble into an abyss of sky.

Okay—scootch closer.

Oooooh...fuck!

It's the micro-dose of psylocibin mushrooms that J. offered you two weeks ago. He said to take it when the moment called for. "You'll know" were his exact words. Out of sheer stupidity, brashness, or perhaps some hidden penchant for reckless abandon, you decided that *this* would be a fine and dandy *day* to take the mushrooms...and...eh, a bit more than a micro-dose.

Jumper three—go!

Jumper four—go!

You watch two more fools tumble into infinity.

The problem, you see, isn't the jumping—it's that the psylocibin peaked...just as the Twin Otter jump plane peaked. So, not only are you about to jump out of an aircraft for the first time in your life. You're about to jump out of your—

Jumping out of my head?

What does that even mean?

Out of my head??...

Jumper five—go!

Jumper six—go!

Out of my head!?

Out of my head!?

Scootch more—

Jumper seven—go!

Jumper eight—go!

Oh, fuck.

I'm jumper ni...

You slide along the final inches of the bench and somehow remember to crouch and scoot bent knee into position with your jump guide.

"You ready!?" Josh yells. "Out the door we—"

Jumper nine!

Huh? What?!

Out of my head!?—

Ohhhhhhh crap!—

Out of my head!?—

Go!

Oh, wait—

Shit, sorry.

J. here.

Getting ahead of myself. All of this doesn't happen until Chapter Twenty-seven. And—oops, this is Chapter One.

My bad.

Let's back up a bit, shall we? Let me see...where were we?

Oh right!...

I think *we were here* last time we hung out:

"You hear the sound of an engine and you know a chartreuse Jeep is pulling into your driveway. A few moments later, you hear a knock at the door.

Excited, you rush downstairs and open the door.

"Good morning, Sunshine!" you both shout simultaneously, with laughter on your lips and joy in your hearts.

"You ready to finish this thing?" asks J.

"Abso-fucking-lutely," you reply.

"Wait 'til you see what I have in store for you!" J. says with glee.

You respond seriously, but with a twinkle in your eye:

"You know—six months ago that statement would have scared the shit out of me, but today...well, you're gonna have to try a lot harder than that to get a rise outta me, friend. A lot harder than that..."

"I'll try my best!" J. exclaims with a smile. "I'll try my best."

Inside you are as excited as a basket of six-week-old puppies.

"Let the adventure continue..."

"Let the adventure continue!!"

Well—okay then.

Shall we?

"Let's catch up in the Jeep." J. says.

"Cool," you reply.

"Grab your things. I'll wait for you outside—with you know who."

"Lenny! Sounds good. I'll be out in a minute."

You rush upstairs and grab the medium sized duffle you've been obsessively-compulsively packing and repacking for the last few days.

Arrangements for a part-time house sitter. Check.

Arrangements for a good chunk of time off work. The rest in digital nomad mode. (Gotta love the internet.) Check.

Wad of cash. Check.

Hiking boots. Bathing suit. Rain jacket. First aid kit. Blank journal. Various pieces of camping gear. Check. Check. Check.

What else? What else?

Right!—strange request, per J.: Favorite peanut butter and jelly. Check.

That's it.

Like a mad end-of-the world prepper about to escape an impending apocalypse, you surrender your life to the bare essentials, lock the door to your home, and courageously, fiercely...step outside into the great beyond...

Oh, Jiminy Cricket!

You go back inside. A few moments after folderolling around with your bladder, you're outside again approaching the Jeep.

What the—the Jeep!?

"What the hell did you do to the Jeep!?" You blurt out to J., who is leaning against the left passenger door fiddling with his phone.

"You like!?" asks J.

"It's yellow!" you exclaim.

"Actually, *hellayella* is the technical name" says J.

"But—"

"Because I liked it! Time for a change! Keeps us on our toes! *And* it's every bit as ostentatious as the chartreuse!"

"I do kinda like it."

"It grows on you."

You walk over to the attached trailer, note the open back hatch, and throw in your duffle. Then, excitedly, you tip-toe skip to the Jeep back panel door.

"Is he in there!?"

"Yes—along with—"

You grab the handle and swing open the door.

"Lenny!!!!!!!!!!!!" you exclaim with glee.

Lenny is seated on his kingly royal throne—the flat sturdy section of his favorite branch—enjoying a three hundred sixty degree outside view.

You finger scratch his back. He arches it slightly in response to your affections. He then casts a nonchalant but approving glance your way. High acknowledgement from the lizard god.

292

And then you see it…camouflaged among the other branches of Lenny's perch…

"Ohhhh my! What—who is that!?"

"Who!? would definitely be the appropriate question. That's Ollie! He's an Eastern Screech Owl."

"Oh! Should I close the door? He could fly…"

"He can't fly. He's wounded. Or *was* wounded. He's disabled."

"Ohhhh—poor thing."

"Ha! Don't worry about Ollie. He's perfectly content. We're taking him with us. There's a wounded wildlife center near where we're headed; they specialize in owls. A friend asked me to transport him—long story. I'll fill you in later. You ready!!?? "

You look J. directly in the eyes.

"I am."

J. closes the back hatch door of the Jeep and then ambles over to the front passenger side door and opens it. He throws the keys up and over the Jeep. You barely have time to react before catching them.

"Good. You're driving," he says.

"Well—that hasn't changed," you mutter.

You hop in and start the engine and put it in drive. J. gives you a few meager directions. Something about Interstate 81 South and Alabama. You use your phone to plug in the directions. You're off!

An hour or so goes by and J. says nary a word.

"So, what's the plan?" you squeak out, deciding to break the silence.

J. looks at you. He takes a *long* pregnant pause. Then he takes a big breath. You then notice—*feel*, for the first time on this trip, J.'s tranquillité d'esprit.

"I have no idea. It's all a mystery to me," he retorts.

"Mystery!?" you belch out.

J. remains calm, unbothered.

"Yep. No idea what's next. It's a mystery. *That's* the plan."

You take a minute to let his answer sink in and then, not knowing how to truly respond...

"Oooooo-kay," you say.

Devious and charming, you think. *Devious and charming...*

I have a confession to make.

Yep. Brakes on and pull over.

Yes—*you,* reader-person holding book.

Here it is: I'm *not* psychic, contrary to what you're about to think...

For instance...

You just peeled back the next few pages or scanned the Kindle pages forward (or, at the very least, have been itching to do so) —to see when the chapter ends—because, as first chapters go, this one is getting lengthy.

I'm just aware of shit.

You're slightly antsy and have got the *Is this author gonna deliver the goods or waste my time?* jitters.

I do the same thing. I usually don't trust an author until three or four chapters in.

You're wondering where in the world this spiritual journey could go next, since so much ground was covered in the last book?

That's just an obvious question.

You're concerned that the surprising, gritty, potty-mouthed tone of the last book will be gone or watered down in this second book. What more can he say or write that will surprise, shock, and awe? And with the same amount of detail, care, honesty, and heart?

This is simple movie-book-narrative-part-two-anxiety. Millions of fans suffered from this affliction at the beginning of *The Empire Strikes Back*, *Harry Potter and the Chamber of Secrets*, and *Debbie Does Dallas 2*.

All predictable shit. So, no—I'm not psychic.

I'm simply aware. I'm awake. (Not *woke*—big difference.) My eyes are wide open. I am here. I am now. My sensory perception and situational awareness are dialed to *max*. I am present.

What the fuck are you even talking about!?

Exactly.

Here's what I'm talking about: If you think *Spirituality for Badasses Part 2* is going to be just like *Spirituality for Badasses Part 1*, you're wrong.

Part 1 was logical, orderly, *relatively* safe, straightforward, and understandable. Part 2 will *not* be any of these things. There will be paradox, conundrum, enigma, and quandary. There will be *mystery*.

Fair Warning for Part 2: Do not put on your thinking caps, boys and girls. Throw logic out the door. If you can't handle this—if you can't handle profanity, dancing on the edge of danger, micro-dosing psychedelics, high-octane adventure sports, or feeling deeply uncomfortable in the face of brain-breaking, heart-expanding, and soul-realizing truth, *Do Not Enter.* Here, there be *many* inexplicable fire breathing dragons. You have been warned.

Okay—cool. That was my confession.

The miles pile up as you cruise south on I 81. J. is preoccupied with his phone, making arrangements for places to stay and people to meet, apparently. He's terse on the phone, revealing minimal information in each conversation, so it's hard for you to glean anything other than vague plans. After a while, you stop eavesdropping and settle into the drive.

"There are two locks to pick on the road to becoming a spiritual badass." J. announces out of nowhere.

You glance at him wide-eyed, letting him know you're listening.

"One lock is on the brain or head and the other lock is on the heart. Each lock is unique and to pick each requires a different set of tools. The tools are fairly straightforward: The head lock tools are mostly logical and orderly. The heart lock tools are mysterious and messy."

He pauses and thinks.

"The results of picking each lock are also different. Each lock picked results in a certain amount and quality of energy, attention, and awareness being released."

Another pause.

"During our last adventure, from what I can gather, I do believe you picked the lock on your head. What do you think?"

"So, becoming a spiritual badass is like doing one of those escape room things?" you reply.

J. chuckles. "Yes, the ultimate paradoxical escape room."

J. continues. "Actually, escape rooms—plural. Jumping out of the first room landed you beautifully, smack dab in the middle of awareness, which—correct me if I'm wrong—healed a good bit of your relationship with body, emotion, and mind. But—"

"True that."

"But—there's a part of you that still remains in your head. And now we enter the second escape room. In this escape room, you'll be jumping *completely* out of your head into—

J. pauses, takes a big breath, and lingers in silence.

"Come on man! You're killin' me. Into what?" you implore.

"Into your heart and soul," says J. "Into your heart and soul."

Spiritual Badass Lesson:

"When I was a child, I spoke like a child, I thought like a child, I reasoned like a child. When I became a man, I put aside childish things." —*Bible, Corinthians 13:11*

Welcome to *Spirituality for Badasses Book 2. How to Find Your Heart and Soul Without Losing Your Cool.* Don't say I didn't warn you.

You ready to rock?

Move along…Chapter One, Book 2 has now ended.

Spirituality for Badasses Book 2
How to Find Your Heart and Soul
Without Losing Your Cool

Available January 2023.

Peace out—
J.

Made in the USA
Las Vegas, NV
21 June 2022

50517008R00164